Healthy Living

THE SPIRIT OF SIMPLE LIVING

Healthy Living

SHARON HANBY-ROBIE

Guideposts®
CARMEL, NEW YORK 10512

The medical information provided in *Healthy Living* is of a general nature and should not be used for diagnosis, nor should it be considered a replacement for consultation with a health-care professional. Before starting any new health or exercise program, including using any information found within this book, you should consult with your doctor or other health-care professional as neither the author nor Guideposts can assume responsibility for your health or health care.

Acknowledgments

Every attempt has been made to credit the sources of copyrighted material used in this book. If any such acknowledgment has been inadvertently omitted or miscredited, receipt of such information would be appreciated.

All material that originally appeared in *Daily Guideposts* is reprinted with permission.

Scripture quotations marked (AMP) are taken from *The Amplified Bible*. Copyright © 1965 by Zondervan Publishing House.

Scripture quotations marked (KJV) are taken from *The King James Version of the Bible*.

Scripture quotations marked (NAS) are taken from the *New American Standard Bible*, © The Lockman Foundation, 1960, 1962, 1963, 1968, 1971, 1972, 1973, 1975, 1977. Used by permission.

Scripture quotations marked (NIV) are taken from *The Holy Bible, New International Version*. Copyright © 1973, 1978, 1984 International Bible Society. Used by permission of Zondervan Bible Publishers.

Scripture quotations marked (NKJV) are taken from *The Holy Bible, New King James Version*. Copyright © 1997, 1990, 1985, 1983 by Thomas Nelson, Inc.

Scripture quotations marked (NLT) are taken from the *Holy Bible, New Living Translation*, copyright © 1996. Used by permission of Tyndale House Publishers, Inc., Wheaton, Illinois 60189. All rights reserved.

Scripture quotations marked (RSV) are taken from the *Revised Standard Version of the Bible*. Copyright © 1946, 1952, 1971 by Division of Christian Education of the National Council of Churches of Christ in the U.S.A. Used by permission.

www.guidepostsbooks.com
1-800-431-2344
Guideposts Books & Inspirational Media Division
Developmental Editors: Cristine Bolley and Deb Strubel
Cover design by Wendy Bass
Interior design by Cindy LaBreacht
Photo by Alex Wilson/Digital Vision Ltd.
Typeset by Nancy Tardi
Printed in the United States of America

Contents

Introduction

Pleasant words are as an honeycomb,

sweet to the soul, and health to the bones.

—PROVERBS 16:24 (KJV)

F or centuries humankind has looked for the fountain of youth, hoping to find a mystical spring that holds promise for eternal life and vitality. Of course, it has never been found. What is amazing is that all along the answer was in God's wellspring of wisdom. His pleasant Words are the wellspring that can make us happy, healthy and alive forever! If we would only believe in God's Word, our sins would be washed away and we would find a new eternal life in the future and a joyful perspective for our life here on earth. Perhaps the fountain of youth that we've been searching for is the living water that God promises us when we accept His love.

God's Word provides the best pattern for living a healthy life physically and spiritually. His pattern also keeps us living morally healthy lives. The key to His pattern is obedience. Unless we obey the pattern God sets for healthy living, we will live with the consequences of our own choosing. It is clear that in spite of the fact that we are living in an imperfect world with imperfect bodies, God still wishes us to live the best we can with what we have.

As I began to write this book, it was not my intention to offer you information on one specific aspect or dimension of living a healthy life. Instead, I set out to find the balance by which God wants us to live; He is concerned about the whole person—body, mind and spirit. If we follow the guidelines that the Bible gives for living as whole beings, rather than focusing on just our physical or mental health, I believe we will be the best we can be. This is certainly not a diet or exercise book. But I would be remiss if I didn't include chapters on both of these topics.

Although I am not an expert, I have searched to find basic yet comprehensive information that I hope you will find beneficial. I, perhaps like you, have the advantage of living beyond the years of my youth. That advantage brings with it the opportunity to have learned a little from my own experiences and mistakes and from those around me. After all, we are all in this together. As we grow in age, I hope we can also grow in spirit and share the blessings, the struggles and the wisdom that we have learned in living a life of faith.

As you read, I hope you will consider me a friend walking alongside you, providing gentle reminders, encouragement and information. I purposely have kept the format simple and short because we are all living busy lives. I have added easy tips for your consideration and a short prayer at the end of each section to inspire you to seek the source for your own pattern for a healthful life.

As we continue our walk together, remember that this is a spiritual journey for an eternal life. The life we have here is temporary and short. Our next will be an eternal life where we will be made anew and experience joy without end. In the meantime, let's learn to accept the life we were given and take care of what we have while keeping our eye on the goal of eternal life.

Consider this your personal working guide for a healthy new life here on earth based on biblical teachings. As we cover each aspect of a healthy life, you will need to take a personal inventory from time to time; this means focusing on you and how you are doing through this process.

As Ephesians 5:15–16 (NIV) says, "Be very careful, then, how you live—not as unwise but as wise, making the most of every opportunity, because the days are evil." As you read and learn new things, or revisit ideas of old, make the most of this opportunity to live more wisely and healthfully. As we learn to see ourselves with a new perspective, our lives will improve. For example, our relationship problems will diminish when, after taking a personal inventory, we are able to admit our wrongs and promptly resolve misunderstandings.

As we learn to express ourselves honestly, we will become more confident, and our true selves will finally shine because we will no longer need to hide behind a façade. We will learn that expressing our real feelings is an enriching way to communicate. As we admit our wrongs, others may be encouraged to look at themselves and discover their own misbehavior. This too can lead to a better understanding for all involved. A personal inventory isn't just about our failures—it's also about our successes. As you read and grow, be sure to give yourself a pat on the back when you realize you are doing something well.

Sometimes it is easy to feel obligated to pick up the slack for others, no matter whose responsibility it really is. But when we learn God's plan, we will be able to put aside the role of world caretaker and allow others to grow as well. When we allow others to learn responsibility for themselves, we become teachers rather than mere doers. And as we learn to turn the care of others over to the Higher Power, we can be assured that they are being loved and supported by the best. God did not design you to provide for everyone's needs. That is His job. Ultimately, we are responsible for ourselves and for how we live this life. And I, for one, think that is a lofty goal on its own.

As you read, my desire is that you will learn to rely more on the love of our ever-present God. He brings order to our lives when we give Him control. With God in control we will be able to contribute to life in more meaningful ways. As our confidence for life and our future increases, our fears will diminish and we will feel the true joy that comes from living a simply healthful life with the people we love.

—*Sharon Hanby-Robie*

Healthy Living

PART ONE

You Are Wonderfully Made

WHEN GOD FORMED YOU, He delighted in everything about you. He gave

you an amazing physiological system to serve you with good health. The

first step to healthful living is learning to accept and nurture the wonder-

ful body you have been given to enjoy. Good habits lead to a good life,

and learning to listen to warning signals in your body will guide you to

change bad habits when needed. Take this first step to enjoying good

health, and simply receive the rest God gives you. Even if you must deal

with an illness, these steps will help.

Love the Skin You're In

I will praise thee; for I am fearfully and
wonderfully made: marvellous are thy works;
and that my soul knoweth right well.

—PSALM 139:14 (KJV)

Of this I am certain, God's perfection goes into the creation of every one
of us. The Bible says that we are made in the image of God, and David,
the psalmist and king of Israel, spoke of God's attention to every detail of our
lives when he wrote, "For you created my inmost being; you knit me together in
my mother's womb. . . . My frame was not hidden from you when I was made in
the secret place. . . . your eyes saw my unformed body. All the days ordained for
me were written in your book before one of them came to be" (Psalm 139:13,
15–16, NIV).

David went on to say that God's thoughts for us are so vast that they outnum-
ber the grains of sand (verses 17–18). Yet I believe that all of us have experienced times when we felt worthless or perhaps even instances when we almost
hated ourselves. But God thought so much of us that He designed our bodies with

the ability to house His own character in the form of the Holy Spirit. The apostle Paul wrote to early believers, "Do you not know that your body is a temple of the Holy Spirit, who is in you, whom you have received from God? You are not your own; you were bought at a price. Therefore honor God with your body" (1 Corinthians 6:19–20, NIV).

As people of faith, we are blessed because we know God's Spirit is ready and willing to work within us to help combat the negative feelings that tempt us to dislike ourselves. The least we can do is to have as much respect for ourselves as our Creator does. This means we must learn to respect and love ourselves, bodies included.

Trust me, as I sit here in a fifty-something body, I believe it would be a whole lot easier to love a twenty- or even thirty-something body. But God doesn't put age limits on whether or not we are to love ourselves.

However, I am sure you remember at least a day when you hated your teen body as well. I know I did. I was a skinny, scrawny kid waiting to grow into an adult body like my mom's. Unfortunately, that never happened. I only got my mother's genes for feet—not her five-foot-seven-inch stature. That translated into short with big feet! The reality is that all of us can find numerous things we dislike or even hate about ourselves.

I recently complimented a woman on her beautiful, curly red hair. Her response surprised me. As she thanked me for the compliment she relayed how it had taken her until her midforties to accept the fact that she has curly hair. She fought to make it straight for most of her life. Now that she has accepted her hair in all its natural beauty, she has gained the simple delight of wash-and-go hair!

As a study by David M. Garner noted, "For the past three decades, women and, increasingly, men have been preoccupied with how they look.

But the intense scrutiny hasn't necessarily helped us see ourselves any more clearly. While as individuals we are growing heavier, our body preferences are growing thinner."[1] That's not a surprise considering the fact that since World War II most popular media have increasingly held up a thinner and thinner body (and now evermore physically fit) image as the ideal for women.

Gerald Jampolsky and Diane Cirincione, founders of Centre for Attitudinal Healing wrote, "One of the most difficult challenges that human beings have is to look into the mirror and say, 'I love you with all my heart, just as you are.'"[2]

There have been a multitude of studies on the media's effect on young girls and teens. In a survey of girls nine and ten years old, forty percent of those interviewed have tried to lose weight, according to an ongoing study funded by the National Heart, Lung and Blood Institute.[3] A 1996 study found that the amount of time an adolescent watches soaps, movies and music videos is associated with their degree of body dissatisfaction and desire to be thin.[4] One author reports that at age thirteen, fifty-three percent of American girls are "unhappy with their bodies." This grows to seventy-eight percent by the time girls reach seventeen. What makes this even more disconcerting is the fact that the image we form as teens can become a part of our lifelong conception of our physical selves. For example, if you thought your hips were too big as a teen, you may continue thinking they are too big long into your adult years, regardless of whether or not it's true.

And the effect of the media doesn't necessarily stop in our teen years. Today, middle-aged and even senior adults are often portrayed in commercials and movies with unrealistic body images. Proof of this is only a reality television show away. Why is it so entertaining to watch men and women undergo intense and dangerous surgery in attempts to attain their idealized, desired image? It's one thing to strive to be the best we can be, but we must learn to love and accept ourselves as we are before we can contemplate the changes that might be made with the cut of a surgeon's knife.

SELF-ACCEPTANCE BEGINS WITHIN

During the teenage years of a friend of mine, when her lower jaw began to protrude beyond her upper jaw, she suffered the embarrassment of being teased by her peers for her appearance. Trusting God had a purpose for making her "different," she overcame her temptation to feel inferior and became a person who was sensitive to the needs of her classmates and was loved by many of them.

Later in life, a dentist told her that she would need to have her bite corrected or else she would lose her teeth prematurely, and she would not even be able to wear dentures! After a two-year process of preparing the alignment of her teeth, the specialist reset her jaw by cutting away the excess bone that caused her malocclusion. When the doctor handed her a mirror so she could see her "look," he asked what she thought of her appearance.

"It's the way I've always seen myself," she replied happily. "Thank you for making it a reality."

Her doctor was amazed at her response. He explained that many times when he had done extensive reconstructive surgery, the patients say, sadly, that they can't see any difference when they look in the mirror. Their self-image was so tied to a negative perception of themselves that even the modern miracle of reconstructive surgery couldn't give them a new expectancy for their future. This is an important lesson for those who think that they can't love themselves until they find a way to make outward changes.

Although body image is often thought of as an aspect of physical appearance, it is far more important because it is the mental representation of ourselves. Our self-image can be influenced by our personal feelings, emotional state or media, and a negative body image can take root and actively influence our behavior as well. The sad reality is that the effects of body dissatisfaction can be very serious and result in eating disorders that may lead to either dangerously underweight or overweight individuals who lack confidence and suffer from profoundly low self-esteem and even clinical depression. Most severe cases require hospitalization, sometimes repeatedly. And it goes even further: Ultimately, self-image can affect our life goals, our ability to function in society and even our choice in life partners.

More than ninety-five percent of all women don't have the "ideal" body type portrayed by the media. A friend and I were discussing the fact that American women are unique because unlike our European counterparts who are mostly one ethnic makeup, we are not. The French women are known for their petite frames with virtually no meat on their thighs. The German gals got the height. The Italians have their curves. Polish women have strong thighs. And Americans have a mix of all parts.

The good news is that you are not the sum of your individual parts: you are a unique person with a wonderful array of special gifts and talents. You are *fearfully and wonderfully* made. As comedian Billy Crystal says, "You look mahvelous darling—simply mahvelous!"

The better news is that you can change your perception of your body. Positive thinking is an essential part of healthy living, and it directly affects your physical and mental well-being. Accepting and loving your body is about friendship. It is about being your own best friend, the kind of friend that you can trust no matter what—a friend who never hurts you and always forgives you. As the dancer Martha Graham says, "The body is a sacred garment. It's your first and last garment; it is what you enter life in and what you depart life with, and it should be treated with honor."

There is a new world of possibilities waiting for you. As you learn to better accept your body, its genetic attributes and how it ages, you will find happiness. And that is one of the best attributes anyone could have.

S I M P L I C I T Y   M A D E   S I M P L E

Here are some ideas to help you get on the path to a simple healthy body image:

Remember that **YOUR BODY IS A MIRACLE**. Regardless of physical condition, age or any limitations, your body is still an incredible machine. It has one hundred trillion cellular citizens living in a harmonious kingdom of sixty thousand miles of blood vessels; a formidable immune system that skillfully eliminates many kinds of unhealthy invaders; an unbelievably efficient heart pump that beats nonstop 2.5 billion times in an average life; and a three-pound brain that serves as a supercomputer with up to one hundred billion nerve cells of lightning-fast memory. God created your body just for you. It is a gift. Honor it—spirit and skin alike.

ACCEPT AND LOVE YOUR BODY as it is, and treat it as a dear friend. Then you will find it easier to feed, rest and exercise it in health-promoting ways.

LISTEN to your body. Don't ignore signals that would otherwise warn you of trouble. Simply take a few minutes each day to consider what your body is saying, whether it's a pain in the wrist or a signal of hunger. Just as you would not ignore the cries of a friend, you shouldn't ignore the cries of your body. Persistent pain is a warning signal that something needs to change. Get professional help when you need it.

Every decade or so it's time to **TREAT YOURSELF TO A MAKEOVER**. One of our town's matriarchs insists on wearing the hairdo she had forty years ago. It has reached the point that there is a comment about it whenever she appears in the paper. You really shouldn't try to wear the same hairstyle, clothes or shoes for a lifetime. If you are unsure of what style of clothes is best for your body type today, enlist the help of a personal shopper. You can find these specialists at many department stores. Learn to wear clothes and hairstyles that make you happy, comfortable and satisfied. This will translate into making you feel better.

INTERRUPT CRITICAL THINKING. Anytime you find yourself falling into the old habit of critical thoughts regarding your body, turn your attention to something else or respond with loving, positive thoughts about your unique attributes.

Pay attention to how your emotional state affects your personal perception of your body. Some people think more negatively when under stress. You can counteract this by finding ways to calm and **REASSURE YOURSELF**. By treating your anxiety and distress, you can improve your body image as well.

Choose to focus on your positive attributes rather than on what you perceive to be negative. **VISUALIZE** yourself *feeling* the way you want to feel. You don't have to change your body to feel good, you just have to get comfortable in the skin you have.

Lord, I believe that You have a purpose in Your design of me. Help me to love the creativity of Your handiwork that You have openly displayed in me.

You're Only as Old as You Think

Gray hair is a crown of splendor;

it is attained by a righteous life.

—PROVERBS 16:31 (NIV)

The Hebrew people believed that a long life was a sign of God's blessing. If you reached the age of white hair, it was considered a very good thing. Young people may have strength, but old people have experience and wisdom that only aging can bring.

When I turned fifty, my mother sent me an odd but beautiful bouquet of flowers. It was a mix of roses and lilies. When I called Mom to thank her for them, she asked if I understood the symbolism that they represented. I did not. She then asked me, "For what particular event does our family send lilies?"

Half in shock, I responded, "Funerals!"

She said, "That's right. The lilies represent the death of your old life and the roses represent the beginning of your new life of experienced wisdom."

I was extremely touched by Mother's memorable gift of flowers and wisdom. I am blessed to have known both my grandmothers and great-grandmothers. All of them were beautiful. I never thought about their appearance; it was their spirits, their hearts and their lives that made them so attractive. Great-grandma Rose never spoke a word of English. Yet I could sit entranced at her feet cherishing every word as she told me of her life and taught me what she had learned from it. As Grandma translated Great-grandma Rose's Hungarian into English, I learned the true meaning of faith, strength and courage. I never once heard her talk about being old. I found her to be simply amazing. She came to America with ten children in tow, no longer willing to wait until Great-granddad was ready for them to come join him.

I come from a long line of women who are comfortable with who they are, never allowing age or gender to stop them from doing anything they wanted to do. At the time of this writing, my mother is seventy-one, and she still works four days a week. We are best friends. She is funny, articulate, wise and up to date. Sure, she wishes her skin didn't show so much age, but who doesn't?

Mother ignores society's belief that age determines who we are, what we can do and how we should look. She believes she is more than her physical limitations and is happy—not wealthy, not young, but happy with who she is. She has accepted herself with the kind of grace that allows her to forgive herself for her mistakes and to make the best of what and who she is.

My mother's attitude is a good one for us to follow. In a culture obsessed with age, it is hard not to define ourselves accordingly. The unfortunate result is that we may miss opportunities because we *think* we are too old.

Do you let your age influence your decisions or actions? I'm not talking about going out and doing something reckless, but things within reason. How many women do you know who act older than they are? How many do you know who act younger? Which kind do you want to be?

I once read an interesting fact that when women marry younger men, they usually adapt to their husbands' age. The opposite wasn't true for men. This encourages me, because it tells me we women can change our perception of age with our attitude. We may still be old chronologically, but we don't have to feel or act it.

Recently, the Senior Olympics were held in my hometown of Cleveland, Ohio. I read about a woman there in her late eighties who holds the senior shot-put record. In addition to throwing the shot put, she runs the one-mile dash! Looking at her picture, it was obvious that she is strong in spite of her age. When she was asked how she does it, she simply said she always had, and just because she got older didn't mean she had to stop. She even works twenty-five hours a week to help pay for the cost of her sport and competition travel expenses!

In his book *The Road Less Traveled*, M. Scott Peck says that the journey of spiritual growth requires courage and initiative and independence of thought and action. The blessings of age are attained only if they also include the growth of our faith. It is only when we are able to integrate a mature spiritual life into our physical life that we can really be complete. Unless we are complete, we cannot be happy. Proverbs 4:7–10 tells us that wisdom is supreme. If we listen to it, we will be blessed with a rich, full life. To quote Peck, "Those who have grown the most spiritually are those who are experts in living. And there is yet another joy, even greater. It is the joy of communion with God."[5]

An unknown author once said, "There is nothing wrong with looking back at the previous seasons of our lives. But God has a purpose for allowing us to be in the season we're in right now. So enjoy where you're at on the way to where you're going."

THERE WILL ALWAYS BE NEW HORIZONS TO REACH

When my grandfather was near the end of his life, he often said he couldn't understand what God was waiting for because Granddad was willing and ready to go. I remember telling Granddad that if there was no reason on earth for him to still be here other than to pray for his grandchildren, that was reason enough! So pray he did.

One woman named Mary Lou Minard of Green Bay, Wisconsin, didn't let being over the hill stop her from starting a new business. At fifty-one she left a steady job to start a cookie business. She and her husband had prayed about it. But it wasn't until her husband came to her with a newspaper ad for an entrepreneur business course that she knew for sure that God was saying yes. When she signed up for the class, she found herself surrounded by other budding entrepreneurs, most of them half her age. At the end of the course, she was the winner of a twenty-five hundred dollar seed money check.

The consistent message seems to be that it's all about what you think. Your attitude toward life and yourself is the deciding factor of how you will cope with growing old. We may not be able to escape the challenges of aging, but we can view each day as a gift full of possibilities.

SIMPLICITY MADE SIMPLE

Here are some simple thoughts to help you adopt your new attitude:

PAY ATTENTION TO YOUR DREAMS. Like Mary Lou Minard, who courageously followed her heart's desire late in life, if you can't let go of a beautiful daydream, then maybe it is time you turned it into reality!

BE COMFORTABLE, especially in the clothes you wear. I know for sure I no longer want to pour myself into a pair of too-tight jeans. A little stretch goes a long way. Wear clothes and hairstyles that allow you to move freely and stay energized for the things you want to do each day.

Approach birthdays with an attitude of gratitude. If making a big deal out of your birthday just makes you feel worse, then try planning to do something to lift your morale instead. The book *Simple Living for Women* suggests starting a birthday book to **RECORD MEMORIES** that you enjoy.[6] Each birthday write down specific blessings you have received throughout the previous year.

SPEND TIME with people who are older than you. My friend Muriel is the best at making and keeping friends of all ages. I have had the pleasure of her wise company for over thirty years and I wouldn't have missed a minute of her unique, sassy, savvy personality. Muriel exemplifies aging with beauty and grace. I only hope I can do half as well as she has.

Surround yourself with **POSITIVE SUPPORTIVE FRIENDS** who enjoy their lives. As the song goes, a friend is a friend forever. For women, it is particularly important to have friends as they age. Statistically, women live longer than men and that means many of them will become widows. Having a strong support group of friends is critical to enjoying a long life.

Use your own trials for the good of others. God is good; He brings us through the trials of life. I believe that each of us has an obligation to **HELP OTHERS THROUGH TRIALS SIMILAR TO OUR OWN**. For example, if you are a cancer survivor, you have an opportunity to help others get through it too.

Aging equals freedom. One advantage to being older is you usually have fewer family responsibilities. **USE THIS NEWLY FOUND FREEDOM** that comes through aging to pursue interests that you didn't have time for before. If you've always wanted to take singing lessons, then take them. Who cares if you can hold a note or not; you're doing this for yourself—not an audience. If you've always wanted to travel, then sign up to become a part of Elderhostel. Elderhostel is a not-for-profit organization and the world's largest educational and travel organization for older adults. Their toll-free number is 877-426-8056.

TEACH OTHERS what you know. Perhaps you have specific knowledge that can be taught; it may be a great time for you to begin teaching. Contact your local community college and offer to teach a course.

Remember that age is mainly about **YOUR ATTITUDE**. Look after your physical health, and adopt a can-do attitude. You are what you believe. If you believe you can do it, you probably can.

> Lord, I believe that the days ahead will be better than the days behind me. Help me to live wisely and make the most of every opportunity that is ordained by You for me to enjoy.

Adopt Good Habits

Confess your faults one to another, and pray one for
another, that ye may be healed. The effectual fervent
prayer of a righteous man availeth much.

—JAMES 5:16 (KJV)

W hen I was first approached to write this series, I discussed the topic with my friend Rochelle, who has given intense attention to her health recently. She immediately suggested that I read *The Twelve Steps of Alcoholics Anonymous* and *The Twelve Steps—A Spiritual Journey*. This is the same woman who less than two years ago was destroying her life through an addiction to alcohol.

Rochelle is an extremely intelligent woman who was able to function in spite of her serious drinking problem. She had reached the point of needing a drink at 9:00 A.M., and often woke up not remembering the night before. I could no longer let my fear of her response keep me from confronting her. I love her and her daughter, but I realized I had begun to play the role of enabler and rescuer when I helped her find a new job after she was fired for drinking on the job. I knew that a real friend would help her get sober. One of the hardest things I ever had to do was to confront her about her lifestyle. I helped her establish a deadline to attempt to work it out on her own or get into a detox program.

It has been a difficult process but Rochelle has put forth the effort and has been clean and sober for over a year. In spite of this success, she recognizes that she must continue to attend her support group or she could easily head down that old road again. When I read in the Scriptures that we are to confess our faults and pray for one another, I realized how important it is for us to admit our weaknesses, bad habits and addictions not only to God but also to our friends and family. Without the support of the "group," we too can easily convince ourselves that we are doing just fine and no longer need to worry about our particular sin.

Yes—sin; whether we like it or not, addictions to food, smoking, drinking, television, the Internet, game playing, whatever, are sins if they control us. In God's kingdom, every believer is a priest to other believers. We have an obligation to help others not only come to Christ but also to learn of His forgiveness and healing power. In a way, we are all like Rochelle, incapable of breaking bad habits alone. To truly recover, we need the love, support and forgiveness of those who care about us.

EXAMINE YOUR HABITS

Obviously, not all of us struggle with issues as big as Rochelle's, but there are other things that we do or don't do every day that affect our health and the health of our families. For example, did you know that something as simple as brushing your teeth three times a day can make a huge difference in the health of your teeth, gums and *heart*. It's true; the bacteria that causes plaque on your teeth is the same bacteria that causes the plaque that blocks your arteries!

Caroline Genco of Boston University's medical school said that infecting mice with the microbe that causes periodontal disease more than doubles the amount of blockage in their arteries, compared with uninfected mice. Genco said the study, presented to the Interscience Conference on Antimicrobial Agents and Chemotherapy, is the first clear evidence that preventing or curing periodontal disease, which is known in its less severe form as gingivitis, also can reduce the inflammation that leads to such ailments as atherosclerosis. Genco's studies explain that periodontal disease, which is caused by a microbe called porphyromonas gingivalis, is common among people over forty, and often begins colonizing the human mouth around the age of twelve or thirteen.

As you examine your daily habits, take into consideration why you do what you do. Wise observers realize that most of us frequently respond out of habit rather than because we have consciously decided this is the best way to handle the situation. Often there are better ways and it's only a matter of learning new behaviors. Basically, there are three ways we learn new habits: by observing others who may have a better way of doing things; utilizing self-talk in advance of falling into our old ways; or through repeated practice until the habits become established.

For example, my friend Marie was habitually late. Come rain or shine, she was always late. Eventually it began to take its toll on her work, her friendships and her relationship with her daughter. Finally she admitted that she had a problem. She realized that it was something she started doing as a child; it was simply a response, however misguided, that made her feel in control. When she was able to acknowledge her lateness, and apologize to all of us who were affected by it, she was finally able to begin to work on changing it. By simply allowing herself ten to twenty minutes more time to get ready, she was able to be on time.

Before we can begin practicing our new habits, we must first know exactly what we are going to do and how we are going to behave. Sometimes it is just a matter of changing your learned response from being late to being punctual, from being impulsive to being careful, from criticizing to giving compliments, from being alone to socializing, from being a late sleeper to being a 6:00 A.M. jogger. There are simple habits that can help or hurt the way we live.

Start by selecting a part of your life that needs to improve and consider a wide variety of alternative responses. Then make a list of possible new responses. If you are struggling to list new ways of coping, ask friends or find a book on your specific area of struggle. You may be surprised at what you already know and only need to put into practice.

Most habits are linked with an ingrained *thought* process. We *tell* ourselves how to behave with the way we think about a particular situation. This is known as Cognitive Behavior Therapy (CBT), which is a process that helps us modify our thinking so we can change our behavior.

Behavior therapy helps us weaken the *connections* between troublesome situations and our habitual reactions to them—reactions such as fear, depression or rage, and self-defeating or self-damaging behavior. It also teaches us how to calm our mind and body, so we can feel better, think more clearly and make sounder decisions.

Cognitive therapy teaches you how certain *thinking patterns* are causing your symptoms by giving you a distorted picture of what's going on in your life, and making you feel anxious, depressed or angry for no good reason, or provoking you into ill-chosen actions.

Behavior therapy and cognitive therapy provide you with very powerful tools for stopping your symptoms and getting your life on a more satisfying track. It is your personal awareness of your thoughts that helps you succeed at developing new habits. Whether your bad habits are simple or complex, the solutions are all a matter of choices.

SIMPLICITY MADE SIMPLE

Here are some ideas to help you improve your life by making better choices:

Prepare for changes by **SPENDING TIME WITH GOD** for guidance. God gives you the ability to choose, but He will make a clear path that leads to a better life. When I was trying to quit smoking, I had a long talk with God. He does have a sense of humor. When I finally said I was willing to quit, not necessarily ready but willing, I developed an odd habit of sneezing just once every time I lit a cigarette. I believe that it was God's way of reminding me that I was supposed to stop. I would laugh and acknowledge His humorous reminder. I was able to quit within a week!

STOP *UN*INSIGHTFUL THINKING. For example, if you are an overeater, you may tell yourself that you don't have the willpower to cut down. The reality may be that you are simply using that statement as an excuse because you haven't taken the time to plan what you are going to eat. If you change your eating environment to one that is conducive to weight loss, you will lose weight.

LEARN TO RECOGNIZE when your thinking is leading you down the old road to destructive habits. Your self-talk can make excuses, rationalize your responses, cause depression and be self-defeating. As you correct those thoughts, you will be able to behave more reasonably and get successful results in your life.

Commit to at least six weeks of time and patience to change or **LEARN NEW HABITS**. Keep a journal about how you feel regarding the changes. Focus on God's faithful truths. You are created in His image, and He wants you to have a more abundant life. You are not alone, the Holy Spirit is walking every step with you.

Father, I repent of destructive habits that hinder the full life
You meant for me to enjoy. Please strengthen me when I am
tempted to live unhealthy patterns and give me understanding
and knowledge that lead to healthy choices.

Keep a Simple Maintenance Plan

In all labor there is profit,

But mere talk leads only to poverty.

—PROVERBS 14:23 (NAS)

As we wear ourselves out with the different roles we play, it's no wonder we find little time to focus on taking care of ourselves. Yet with just a few simple steps we can gain a "little profit" physically. We can improve our circulation, curb our appetites, lower our risk for several diseases and even improve our sleep. Ah . . . a good night's sleep. . . . Wouldn't that be nice? I'll talk more about sleep and diet later in the book. This section is about getting some exercise to keep you from the poverty level physically.

First things first: When is the best time to exercise? That depends a lot on you and your schedule. But many experts say that late afternoon hours, between 2:00 P.M. and 4:00 P.M. are best. Studies have shown that at this time of day your body temperature is at its peak, which is one to two degrees higher than in the morning. According to the American Council on Exercise, your muscles are warmer and more flexible, and your reaction time is quicker. Your strength is also at its height. These are the optimum conditions for working out. In a perfect world, this is the best time to exercise.

However, finding time in the middle of the day is not an option for most of us. Besides, yet another study found that women who exercised for thirty minutes each *morning* slept better at night. For me, if I don't do it first thing in the morning, it's probably not going to happen.

What's the best kind of exercise? That too depends on you. I'm a walker. It is the only exercise that I have found I can do consistently. My friend Jan and I have walked together for nearly ten years, with the exception of last year when we both found our lives at a pace that simply didn't leave room. The unfortunate thing is that one year of not walking made me feel five years older. Walking is one of the easiest and best things you can do for your body. Doctors say a cardiovascular workout is great for your heart, fitness trainers say it's a fine way to lose your tummy, and physical therapists will tell you it strengthens your back. How's that for a power workout? Jan and I walk outdoors at a park when weather permits, and we walk indoors at a skating rink when the weather is bad. As the old proverb advises: "From walking—something; from sitting—nothing."

The best part of walking with a friend like Jan is that it's a great time for soul talk. In addition, we are burning calories. Did you know that if you walk a mile in twenty minutes, you burn .027 calories per pound per minute? That means if you weigh 150 pounds and walk a twenty-minute mile for sixty minutes, you burn 270 calories. That leaves you enough calories to have dessert! It's no wonder that walking continually ranks as the top fitness activity among women.

Nearly eighty million Americans walked for exercise in 2003 (compared to twenty-three million that jogged). Because walking is low impact, risks are minimal. Regular walkers actually have less chronic illness. Dr. JoAnn Manson, a professor of medicine at Harvard Medical School says, "Women can literally walk away from heart disease and diabetes." Brisk walking raises heart rates enough to create a beneficial cardiovascular workout.

If walking isn't your cup of tea or you don't feel up to it physically, try Tai Chi. It's not as beneficial from a cardiovascular and weight management standpoint, but it is great for flexibility and joint problems. Tai Chi is an ancient Chinese exercise system that takes your arms and legs through slow, graceful moves. People of all ages and fitness levels can safely do Tai Chi. I signed up for a class when I was struggling with some major physical ailments that prevented me from doing much of anything else. It's great for balance because the movements are structured—a little like ballet.

It's all about aligning your body in precise positions that improve coordination and require mental focus. This is great for tuning your body as well as your mind. In a one-hour class of Tai Chi you can gain flexibility, increased muscular strength, improved balance and posture and enhanced muscle tone. And I promise you that you can do it. In fact, many experts recommend Tai Chi for chronic pain, reducing stress and lowering blood pressure.

STAY TRUE TO YOURSELF

What's the most important thing you can do for your health? Tell the truth! Did you know that fifty percent of patients admit that they lie to their doctors? It's true. We want our doctors to think we are good people. So we lie about things that can affect our doctor's ability to give us proper care.

Many folks are shy when it comes to talking about personal issues. So they don't tell their doctors about the *little* bladder problem they are having. They convince themselves it's not a big deal, or when speaking with their primary care physician they conveniently forget to list the medicine their gynecologist prescribed.

Alcohol is probably the thing that gets lied about the most. Although health officials say that there are some antioxidant benefits in red wine, there is still a drawback to the alcohol content. It's not okay to keep information about alcohol consumption from your doctor. Did you know that alcohol can cause liver damage when mixed with high doses of acetaminophen such as Tylenol? It can.

I'm a cancer survivor. I had uterine and cervical cancer at the age of twenty-eight. That was a huge wake-up call for me. Since that time, I have become a sponge when it comes to information about health issues. One of the most misdiagnosed cancers is ovarian cancer. The symptoms are often ignored by us and the doctors. One classic symptom is an abdomen that rather suddenly enlarges with the added problem of constipation and/or diarrhea. (There are other symptoms, so if you are concerned, go see your doctor.)

I know a woman who looked as if she was four or five months pregnant. She first started a diet and exercise regimen, thinking she was just going through midlife tummy bulge. Finally, with no results, she went to the doctors who took X-rays of her abdomen. She was diagnosed with Irritable Bowel Syndrome (IBS). Many months later, she was still not doing well. She was finally diagnosed with the results from a simple CA-125 blood test. At least she knows what she is up against, but it was unfortunate that it was not detected sooner. She is still fighting cancer, and I continue to pray for her.

Personally, I think the CA-125 blood test should be part of a regular yearly physical. But your insurance provider may not agree. There is research that suggests that it doesn't correctly detect cancer in all cases, and that it should be used in conjunction with a pelvic exam and sonogram with high-risk women or anyone showing the typical symptoms. This means that if you want it you will pay for it. But it is a simple test and is certainly worth asking your doctor about it.

Total well-being is physical, spiritual and psychological wellness. The Bible teaches us how to renew our minds for psychological health, and affirms that God is the source of spiritual *and* physical health. Modern medicine has rediscovered the relationship between the two. To be physically healthy we must also have a close relationship with God. The Scriptures offer moral prescriptions that include having self-control over what we eat and how we care for our bodies. We are to view our bodies as temples of the Holy Spirit, which should include regular maintenance. I know that just like a car, the older I get, the more maintenance I need.

SIMPLICITY MADE SIMPLE

Here are some tips to help you maintain your frame:

FIND YOUR EXERCISE STYLE whether you choose to walk, take part in a sport, clean your house (yes, this can count as a form of exercise), garden, swim or bike. The key is to choose something you enjoy enough that you will stick to it.

FIND A PARTNER to make exercise a habit, and alternate your routine: walk one day and dance another. By adding a little salsa music, you can quicken your pace to good health!

STAY POSITIVE; all good things take time. If you don't see results right away, be patient. When I first started exercising it took four to six weeks before I could notice any changes.

You can **FIND TIME**. You can exercise while watching television, bike to the store or play Frisbee with your dog. Park your car at the far end of the parking lot when you go to work or shop. Get to work ten minutes early and walk around the building!

Don't forget about **BREAST HEALTH**. Do a breast self-examination at the same time each month. If you are menstruating, do it after your period has ended. A mammogram is still the best screen available, though it is not perfect. MRI is becoming more useful in evaluating specific suspicious areas, but it is too expensive to use as a screening device.

CORE STRENGTH is critical to having good balance, and good posture. A strong core will also make all exercise easier. What's a strong core? It's having a strong tummy. To make your midsection stronger, simply pull it in and hold for five seconds several times while brushing your teeth, showering, driving your car or talking on the phone.

To improve **UPPER BODY STRENGTH**, do a couple of wall push-ups. Place your hands at chest level on the wall with your feet several inches behind your body. Then lean forward toward the wall. Slowly push back.

Looking to improve the sight of your **HIPS AND THIGHS**? Raise your leg from your side twelve to fourteen inches and return to the starting position. To tone your rear end, lift one leg toward your back with your knee slightly bent, then slowly return your foot to the floor.

Ultimately, the best tip for an exercise regimen is to **HAVE AN OPEN AND FRANK DISCUSSION WITH YOUR DOCTOR** first, then follow his or her advice.

Father, I know that sickness and pain are consequences
of living in a fallen world. But I look forward
to the day when the whole world will experience
Your healing touch. In the meantime, help me Lord
to care for my body as the temple that it is.

You Are What You Eat

And when the children of Israel saw it, they said
one to another, It is manna: for they wist not what it was.
And Moses said unto them, This is the bread which the
Lord hath given you to eat.

—EXODUS 16:15 (KJV)

Wouldn't it be wonderful if God provided you with miraculous food every-day? Imagine not having to cook or to worry about calories or nutrition—just waiting for the perfect food to show up out of thin air. Now that's what I call cooking with God!

Unfortunately, the reality is that the mere thought of attempting to eat the right things has become much like throwing a dart at a dartboard. Every day, we read yet another "healthy" way to eat. And, of course, there are now numerous studies to prove that milk is good for you, not good for you, will make you thinner, will make you sicker . . . you choose. One thing is for sure, no one knows anymore what to believe.

I think it's interesting that most experts agree that the old-fashioned Middle Eastern diet of biblical times was pretty much right on. Of course it was. Just think about the kinds of foods they ate in the Promised Land: grains such as wheat, barley, millet, and spelt; cucumbers; beans; onions; herbs; garlic; and lentils. Don't forget fruits and nuts: figs, raisins, apples, pomegranates, grapes, olives, pistachios and almonds. Milk products were also essential to the Hebrew diet. And birds supplied eggs and were also eaten as well as locusts. Sheep and cattle were mostly used for sacrifice and only eaten on special feast occasions. But people did hunt and eat antelope, deer, gazelle, ibex, mountain sheep and wild goat. And what about fish? Christ's apostles were fishermen—fish was a huge part of their diet.[7]

How does your daily diet compare to theirs? Unfortunately, even if you are eating as healthfully as they did, most foods today have been reconfigured to no longer contain the nutritional value they once had. For example, if you eat white bread instead of whole-grain floured bread, you may as well eat ice cream because the way your body processes sugars makes it less fattening. And if you get most of your fruits and vegetables from frozen or reconstituted juices, you are losing the nutritional value found in their fresh, unprocessed counterparts.

Food that is whole and intact is always better than chopped, sliced, diced, mashed or pureed. An apple sounds healthy, right? Well it is, but mainly if you eat the apple with the skin on. Most of the soluble fiber is in the skin. Therefore, if you eat the apple, skin and all, your stomach has to contend with the fiber before it can get to the fructose (sugar).

Why is this important? Bottom line, it's all about the glycemic index numbers. The glycemic index measures how fast a food is likely to raise your blood sugar. This is very helpful for managing blood sugar levels, which is a life-saving key not only for diabetics but also for the rest of us. For example, if your blood sugar tends to spike after your "breakfast of champions," you may want to select a cereal with a lower glycemic index. Fiber isn't the only thing that helps slow down the sugar; fats and proteins also slow the speed with which your stomach works on digesting carbohydrates (carbs). Eating a little protein or some beneficial fat like olive oil on your bread, as part of a sensible meal, is actually better for you than bread alone.

Don't forget about what you drink. Many folks actually consume more calories a day by drinking than they do in eating. Dr. Arthur Agatston, author of *The South Beach Diet*,[8] said he had a patient who suddenly began experiencing symptoms of diabetes. His blood sugar shot up to over four hundred! (The target blood sugar range is 80–120 mg/dl.) He didn't have any of the other conditions usually present with diabetes so it took some digging to find out what was going on. It turns out that a juice machine had been installed at his office. In an attempt to cut down on coffee, he switched to serving himself several glasses of orange juice a day. As a result he was dumping too much sugar into his bloodstream. Once he switched to water instead, his blood sugar level returned to normal—though he still must remain cautious about the possibility of diabetes.

Few of us like to even think about dieting. And most of us cannot stick to any strict diet that deprives us of normal eating. Just like the wisdom says, everything in moderation.

If you want to be able to look at your thinner self in the mirror and smile, you must cut down on calories. Try leaving three or four bites on your plate instead of eating every last morsel. If you want to feel better, you have to make healthier choices. And that doesn't necessarily mean choosing frozen diet food meals, because you will likely be hungry once you have finished eating. Our bodies were designed for a balanced diet of carbs, fats, protein and sweets. Good health is about choosing the right kind and right amount of each.

CHOOSE FROM THE MENU THAT LEADS TO LIFE

Many years ago, I was very ill. My doctor gave me a choice: Either restrict my diet to meat, fish, chicken, vegetables and a few grains, or die. Guess which I chose? It's amazing when it comes down to a matter of life and death how disciplined we can be. How we live is a matter of life and death. A healthy long life or an unhealthy short one is very much a matter of the choices we make.

It's not about willpower; it's about planning. The reality is that most of us simply don't take the time to plan our meals, shop for fresh produce and meat or fish, and prepare them. Believe me; I know how hard that can be. But what if you did this simply for three dinner meals a week? Imagine the joy of eating a fresh home-cooked meal with your family three times a week. Not only would you be healthier physically but your family would be psychologically healthier as well.

What it boils down to is that a health-promoting lifestyle of regular exercise and eating well is good for body and soul. God is an abundant provider. He made food to be consumed for sustenance, nutrition and pleasure. And even in the land of milk and honey, a little restraint went a long way.

SIMPLICITY MADE SIMPLE

Here are some tips to help you on your journey to a healthier you:

CUT OUT FLOUR AND SUGAR for two weeks if you are looking for a way to get a quick start to losing weight. Sugar includes fruit. That's right, no fruit for two weeks. For extra added punch to your paunch, give up rice, potatoes and pasta as well for those two weeks and you will find yourself with a smaller waist in no time. But remember, the key to maintaining healthy weight is to establish balanced eating habits that you can maintain for a lifetime.

BUY LEAN CUTS OF MEAT if you want to lower fat in your diet. Avoid regular bacon; instead choose Canadian bacon. Skip the sausage, hot dogs and all lunch meat except turkey breast. If you wish, eliminate meat entirely.

SWITCH TO LOW-FAT or skimmed products if you love your dairy foods. And opt for low-fat cheeses such as Jarlsberg and cottage cheese.

Dr. Alan Hirsche, who is the neurological director of the Smell and Taste Treatment and Research Foundation in Chicago, suggests **USING THE SENSE OF SMELL** to lose weight. In a recent study, participants who sprinkled powders that smelled like cheddar cheese, banana and raspberry on foods lost an average of 5.6 pounds per month over a six-month period. In theory the added scents fool the brain into thinking you have eaten enough. Dr. Hirsche suggests you smell every food before you eat it. My brother has always done this—and I thought he was weird! Who knew?

If you think you are doing your body a favor by drinking sun-brewed tea— **THINK AGAIN.** When tea steeps in the sun for several hours, bacteria can multiply rapidly and pose a risk for illness.

If you are really struggling to get a healthful eating plan, then **TRY ENLISTING THE HELP OF A NUTRITIONIST**. She can help with most health concerns. This is especially helpful if you have specific dietary concerns such as lowering cholesterol, controlling blood sugar, dealing with food allergies or coping with IBS. Some nutritionists will even make a house call to give your pantry and refrigerator a makeover. They will help you toss what you don't need and assist you in preparing a shopping list of healthful foods.

YOUR MORNING MEAL should provide about one-third of your day's caloric intake. For me, having a bowl of oatmeal makes this easy. But do *not* use instant oatmeal because it has been chopped into such fine grains that it is no longer a good source of fiber, thus losing its full value. Instead, take the five minutes needed to make the old-fashioned oats and then enjoy a healthful breakfast.

EAT MORE FIBER. It's the simplest way to stabilize blood sugar levels. Your goal should be twenty-five grams of fiber a day. For example: a cup of lentils, a pear or one slice of whole wheat (preferably whole grain) bread will fulfill this quota.

INCREASE YOUR GREENS! Include spinach and kale regularly; they are rich sources of iron and vitamin A, as well as lutein, which is great for your eyes.

Lord, thank You for giving us a world full of food choices
that are pleasant to our taste and good for our bodies.
Help me to plan balanced meals that will make my body
strong and full of energy to enjoy life.

YOU ARE
WONDERFULLY
MADE

Enjoy a Deep Sleep

I cried unto the Lord with my voice,

and he heard me out of his holy hill. Selah.

—PSALM 3:4 (KJV)

Sleep doesn't come easy during a crisis. When King David's son Absalom rebelled and gathered an army to kill his father, he could have had a few sleepless nights. Instead, David cried out to the Lord, and the Lord heard him. The assurance of an answered prayer always brings peace. It is certainly easier to sleep well when we *accept* God's assurance that He is in control of all circumstances. If you are lying awake at night worrying about your situation, one step toward sleep is a simple prayer of faith.

But what happens when your sleepless nights have nothing to do with worry? There has been many a night when I wished, like Abraham, that God would put me into a deep coma. What a relief that would be from the insomnia that has plagued me most of my life. My mother says they put me on sleeping pills at nine months of age because I literally did not sleep at all. I can say, I don't remember getting even one night's sleep all through college. To this day, I am thrilled when I get a full night of eight hours' sleep.

For most of my life, four or five hours of sleep a night has been my norm. But I consider myself fortunate because it has not affected my energy level. Just last week two friends commented on how they would love to have fifty or even twenty-five percent of the energy I have. Nonetheless, I still find it frustrating to lie awake the entire night while my husband sleeps noisily away. Yes—noisily. He snores. I mean *really* snores.

In fact, when we go camping, I am sure his snoring is what keeps the bears away from our campsite! He definitely has sleep apnea. And he promises that he is going to get help. But it wasn't until I made him read an article on how serious a condition sleep apnea is that he finally accepted the reality of his snoring.

Sleep apnea affects about eighteen million Americans, according to the National Institutes of Health. People with this disorder stop breathing for one to ten seconds at a time, dozens to hundreds of times a night. Though not usually fatal, it may raise blood pressure and the risk of heart attack and stroke. If this is something you or your mate suffers with, please get professional help.

The key to solving this sleep issue is to create "positive airway pressure." After undergoing a complete sleep study including the measurement of brain waves, eye and limb movements and air flow through the body, most can be helped with a sleep mask device called CPAC (continuous positive airway pressure).

Evelyn Waugh, an English writer, said, "I haven't been to sleep for over a year. That's why I go to bed early. One needs more rest if one doesn't sleep."

Sleep is essential to good health. Research has shown that lack of proper sleep can cause problems with concentration, irritability, diminished productivity and possibly increased vulnerability to certain illnesses, including an impaired immune system. According to the National Highway Traffic Safety Administration, more than one hundred thousand crashes annually are the result of drivers falling asleep at the wheel.

SEEK HELP FOR SLEEP DISORDERS

Insomnia is the most common sleep disorder. Some doctors think that one-third to one-half of us endure extended periods of insomnia at some point. It is not a surprise that twice as many women suffer from insomnia as men. Some think it's our fluctuating hormones or our eventual lack of them that contributes to the problem. According to the National Sleep Foundation, doctors wrote more than thirty-five million prescriptions for sleeping pills in 2003. That foundation estimates that three out of four women get less than the recommended eight hours of sleep per night.

Dr. Lydia Wytrzes, a neurologist and director of the Sutter Sleep Disorders Center in Sacramento, California, says, "Many women exist in a state of perpetual sleep-deprivation."

For some sleep-deprived sufferers, it's a matter of having restless legs. Statistics indicate that twelve million Americans have restless leg syndrome (RLS). RLS is a neurological disorder that causes uncomfortable sensations in the legs. The feeling is often described as restless, drawing, itchy, buggy or crawling sensations. Ironically, it gets its name from the fact that the fizzing, sizzling sensation stops with motion. RLS is most common among women. New research suggests that RLS may come from an abnormality in the brain related to low levels of the chemical dopamine, but this is still preliminary. Some sufferers find relief by taking a hot shower or bath before bed. Others find a massage to be their best bet. For chronic cases, a doctor can prescribe dopamine-like drugs that are used to treat Parkinson's disease. Another cause can be anemia. A simple blood test can make this determination, and anemia is easy to correct with a daily iron supplement.

Teeth grinding also robs people of sound sleep. At least five percent of Americans grind their teeth at night. And most of them don't even know they do it, at least not until they wake in the morning with a pained jaw. Amy Ludwig, DMD, a New York City prosthodontist, says, "The constant contraction of the muscles that close the jaw can cause pain and headaches and fracture teeth." She suggests using the tips of your fingers to massage the temple and jaw regions of your face for about five seconds each. This is especially helpful when you awake and throughout the day. You can also try using a warm compress on the jaw. One solution that always helps is to wear an acrylic mouth guard at night. You can have one custom made by your dentist or start by trying one of the over-the-counter mouth guard kits from your pharmacy.

For most of us, it's simply not being able to fall asleep, stay asleep, keep a regular schedule, or find time to get a full night of sleep. Don't despair; there is plenty that you can do to help make sleeping like a baby a reality.

SIMPLICITY MADE SIMPLE

Here are some ideas to guide you to sweet dreams:

Three things that all the experts agree on: a cup of **HERBAL TEA** before bed; a glass of **WARM MILK**, which is my favorite (the tryptophan contained in warm milk lulls you to sleep); and **A COOL BEDROOM**. In the winter, I turn the furnace thermostat down before retiring for the night. If I forget, I struggle to fall asleep or to stay asleep.

Try taking a **WARM BATH** before bed to raise your body temperature. This is my mom's favorite trick. As you cool down afterward, you are more inclined to drop off to sleep.

Keep the bedroom a **SACRED SLEEPING SANCTUARY**. As an interior designer, I am a stickler on this tip that all experts agree helps. No office equipment and no television. Did you know that the bright lights from the TV activate your brain the same way a sunrise does? It's true. When you watch TV late at night, you are actually telling your brain to wake up!

ESTABLISH A CONSISTENT BEDTIME. Go to bed at the same time and wake at the same time if at all possible. I work a swing-shift schedule at QVC, a television shopping network. Sometimes I have shows at 4:00 A.M. A consistent schedule for me is impossible. Regular exercise, a healthful diet, and napping are the keys for folks with a crazy schedule like mine. Catnaps are best. If you try to nap for more than ten to twenty minutes, your muscles start to relax and you may feel worse than if you didn't nap.

DON'T EXERCISE WITHIN TWO HOURS OF BEDTIME. As I noted previously, studies show that women who exercised for thirty minutes in the *morning* slept better at night.

SOME THINGS ARE OBVIOUS, like not consuming caffeine within four to six hours of bedtime. But did you know that the old nightcap ritual is a bunch of nonsense? Although a glass of wine may initially help you fall asleep, it can also disturb deep sleep later on.

Remember the princess and the pea under the mattress? It was one of my favorite childhood stories. I loved the way Carol Burnett played the part on her show. It was hysterical. She piled several mattresses one on top of the other and could still feel that silly pea. **YOUR MATTRESS SHOULD BE REPLACED EVERY TEN YEARS.** The old idea of a rock-hard mattress being good for your back has proven to be a bunch of hooey. The key is finding a mattress that provides support with comfort. A good mattress will cost you between five hundred and two thousand dollars. Don't forget about a proper pillow also. Choose either a good down-filled pillow or one of the ergometrically designed pillows with a scooped out midsection. This is what I use and it has really helped to take the pain out of my neck.

Your doctor can prescribe **A TEMPORARY SLEEP AID**. There are sleep aids on the market today formulated to help you fall asleep within thirty minutes and wear off within a few hours so you don't wake up feeling groggy.

Bottom line, **DON'T LIE AWAKE** all night in bed. You'll just keep obsessing about the time of night it is and never fall asleep. Instead, get up and do something relaxing but do it in dim light. Try listening to soft music, take a soothing bath or read a book—but not a page-turner! The idea is to *relax*. And the best source of peace is still our Maker. Try talking to Him. I always ask Him who needs prayer when I can't fall asleep, and He always has an answer for me. This gets my mind off my own everyday concerns.

> Lord, my soul finds rest in You alone. I put all my cares in Your hands and receive the blessing of sleep that You promise to those You love (see Psalm 127:2).

Cope with Illness

And he said unto me, My grace is sufficient for thee:

for my strength is made perfect in weakness.

Most gladly therefore will I rather glory in my infirmities,

that the power of Christ may rest upon me.

—2 CORINTHIANS 12:9 (KJV)

D id you ever wonder why God afflicted Paul with "a thorn in the flesh"? And why God didn't remove it when Paul asked Him to? Perhaps it was because Paul was strong in his abilities and resources. When we are strong in our own abilities, it is easy to let pride take hold of our lives. God demonstrated *His* power in Paul's weakness. And God promises this same power to all of us, weak or otherwise. This should give us courage in dealing with our own thorns of the flesh.

Relying on God for our effectiveness rather than on our own simple energy, effort or talent is a lesson in humility and faith. Besides, for most of us, our weakness can help us to develop Christian character, deepen our worship and affirm God's strength. I must admit, there have been times when I wondered if I hadn't already endured enough character building. Perhaps I was just stubborn or a slow learner and God had no choice but to bean me over the head to get my attention.

Having cancer at a young age certainly changed my perspective on a lot of things. I learned, for example, the true meaning of praying unceasingly during my bout with cancer. No matter what I was doing, inside I was praying. When your body totally betrays you, faith is the only thing you can rely on. I personally challenged God—out loud! I did not take my sickness lying down. I became extremely proactive, learning all I could about my particular illness. This enabled me not only to make better decisions regarding my treatment but also to have some sense of control.

I think being proactive is an important attitude for coping with illness. Unless we participate in and have knowledge to make good choices, we can be tempted to become "victims" instead of patients. A victim attitude is one of "poor me, life is unfair, and there is nothing I can do," which is never the truth. There is always something you can do, even if it's only accepting the fact that God is ultimately in control and He will provide you with the strength you need if you ask for it; then get on with the life you have.

Paul's illness was not fatal but chronic. He lived with it and had a successful ministry in spite of it. Coping with chronic illnesses can affect you physically, emotionally, socially and sometimes financially. Although it takes time to adjust and accept the realities of a long-term illness, those that participate actively in their own care usually cope the best. Coping is a process. Feeling vulnerable, sad, angry or worried is just the first stage of coping. The second stage is the learning stage. As I said before, knowledge is power. It also helps to remove some of the fear. The unknown is the scariest. Once we have a better understanding of our conditions and know that others are successfully managing with them, we feel less afraid.

The third stage in the coping process is acceptance, which is learning to take an illness in stride. This is the stage where most of us are comfortable with our treatment plan and have learned to use the tools necessary for living a normal life. For example, I know a woman with severe diabetes. She wears an insulin pump on her belt. In spite of her illness she is a wife, the mother of two and has a job that keeps her quite active. For her, managing diabetes is just another daily step like brushing her teeth or showering. For her, it's no big deal. It's just part of her life. And that's critical to being a good patient versus one who allows oneself to be a victim patient.

It's sad to see someone who could otherwise live a normal life choose to be a victim. Or worse yet, to use illness as a weapon of control in family relationships. We have all seen people who play their illnesses like an ace card. Every time they want something, they put on the "poor me, I'm too sick to do this for myself" attitude, expecting others to run to their side and serve them.

There is no limit on how long it will take for someone to come to terms with accepting his or her chronic illness. Each of us is different. And it is not unusual for emotions to resurface from time to time. The key is to recognize and be aware of these emotions when they do emerge so you can move forward once again through the process.

KNOW YOUR STRENGTHS—GIVE YOUR WEAKNESSES TO GOD

The most successful individuals are those who generally have good self-esteem and a realistic understanding of their own strengths and weaknesses. They continue to define personal goals and to find gratification in their accomplishments. They believe that they are valuable and can still have a positive influence on their family and community in spite of their symptoms.

This translates into maintaining hope. And the source of our hope is faith in God. Of course, having strong support from family is an advantage. I found that educating my husband on my illness and the necessary requirements to maintain optimum health made all the difference in the world. He can be truly sympathetic when I say I *must* get some rest, or I have to eat now. Rather than thinking I am being demanding, he understands that this is what I must do to take care of myself.

It's also critical that you have confidence in your health-care providers. I went through five physicians with my cancer treatment before I felt I found one that really listened to me. She was amazing; she heard my heart's cry. And she allowed me to participate and try new methods rather than being forced to follow the conventional protocol. This was important to me. She also allowed my faith to be a part of the healing process. When I said I wanted to just trust God on a particular issue, she stood in agreement with me by making an appointment for six weeks later to evaluate. It was exactly what I needed.

And remember, keeping yourself as stress-free as possible will help your body heal. I was very fortunate to have a strong support group of friends and family that I could count on for what I needed—especially prayer. With the healing of my body came the strengthening of my soul.

SIMPLICITY MADE SIMPLE

Coping skills are as individual as we are. But here are some suggestions to help you live life abundantly even in the midst of illness:

TAKE RESPONSIBILITY for your own health care. Continuously educate yourself about your illness. Stay abreast of new medications and treatments. I subscribe to several health publications. One of my favorites is *Bottom Line Health*.

DEFINE WHAT YOU HAVE LOST. My dad had multiple sclerosis (MS), but he worked with his therapist to maintain his ability as much as possible. He also learned to use aids to help compensate for his physical weakness. By honestly defining his limitations, he was able to get help for what he needed.

WATCH YOUR ATTITUDE AND BEHAVIOR. It can be easy to adopt a negative attitude such as "I can't do it . . . it's hopeless," or "I can't stand it." Such thoughts only increase the burden under which we function. It's also easy to find ourselves being overly passive or dependent on others. This too can develop into an unhealthy pattern for living. Instead, be positive and focus on what you can do rather than what you cannot. Remember, that as we read in Psalm 139:13 (NAS), God formed your most inward parts; He wove you in your mother's womb. You are made exactly as He wanted you to be. He also promises that all of us will have talents—not the same talents—but our own unique talents. Therefore, accept that you are a competent individual with talents and attributes that are inherently yours and will be yours forever, regardless of your illness. Be thankful and flourish.

ACCEPT EMOTIONAL REALITIES. It is normal to be sad, angry or wonder "Why me?" *temporarily*. Over time, most people will come to terms with the new reality of their lives. If you are unable to progress, seek help so you can move forward with your life. Don't let depression set in—it can only exacerbate your situation. Your physician can help you but you have to *ask* for help.

YOU ARE NOT SUPERHUMAN. Don't elect to take on additional burdens or responsibilities to prove how strong you are. This can lead to yet another type of wrong attitude—that of a martyr. Carefully consider your options when taking on responsibilities.

Here are some tips for the spouses of those dealing with chronic illness:

RECOGNIZE that you are not in control or responsible for the behavior of anyone but yourself. Your job is simply to try to make it easier for the patient to behave in a realistic manner.

DON'T AID, ABET OR REWARD BAD BEHAVIOR. Although we cannot know the internal reality of the patient, we can help him or her avoid negative self-fulfilling prophecies. Before you take on more than your fair share of work, check your assumptions. Be sure they are true. For example, are you sure your spouse can't bathe without help, or do basic housework? Encourage a positive attitude and normal life like taking a walk outside, taking a vacation or simply snuggling close with you.

BECOME AN EXPERT in your partner's illness. The more you know, the more help you can be in making the right decisions regarding care and realistic expectations.

MAINTAIN A NORMAL LIFE FOR YOURSELF. It's easy to become the victim of someone else's illness. Accept your own limitations. You are not a miracle worker or superhuman and you shouldn't feel guilty or as though you must carry all the burden and work alone. Even the most loving mates need time for themselves. It's okay to give yourself permission to get a little pampering too!

MONITOR YOUR OWN EMOTIONS. It's just as easy for the mate of the patient to start asking, "Why me?" Friends of ours married young with the full knowledge of the wife's illness. As is not surprising, the naiveté of youth kept the reality of her illness from settling in until many years later as they now attempt to cope with a seriously disabling degenerative disease. Even as the patient experiences losses of independence, health and a bright future, so too does the spouse face these same kinds of losses. This is normal. Try not to let it negatively influence your relationship. Rejection will not benefit either one of you.

Lord, as I face each day and the new reality it brings,
help me to realize that I am not a victim. I am Your
wonderfully made child. Help me to ask for help
when I need it, and to actively participate
in my own care emotionally and physically, seeking
Your grace and strength for every challenge of my life.

PART TWO

There Is a Rhythm to Life

A BALANCE BETWEEN WORK AND PLAY leads to a healthy mind. There are ways to work simply smarter instead of harder so that you have more time for the pleasures of life. Work is a necessary part of our lives—regardless of our ages—but it is possible to work at something that is mentally stimulating as well as fun to do. In this section, we will discuss ways to expand your brainpower and plan better. We'll see how to transform ordinary tasks into spiritually meaningful aspects of our lives. And we will find the joy of play and the blessings that come as we learn to set goals that include our spiritual lives as part of our whole.

49

The Perfect Balance

"Come to Me, all who are weary and heavy-laden,

and I will give you rest."

—MATTHEW 11:28 (NAS)

Take a deep breath, hold it for five seconds, and now slowly release it. Ah . . . don't you feel better? Imagine how much better yet you could feel if you sat down in a garden with God for a full fifteen minutes and allowed Him to regenerate you with His peace, love and healing power. Most of us are overburdened with daily schedules. We live life at warp speed as we attempt to complete the never-ending to-do list.

Have we forgotten that God freed us from such oppression? He promises rest. His burden is light. Not that we won't have work—we will. But having a relationship with God changes the meaningless toil into spiritual productivity and gives it purpose. That simple change can make all the difference in our ability to find balance in our daily lives. By allowing God to be in control of our lives, we can be assured of living a balanced life. He will not lead us to do more than we are capable of doing.

Guideposts writer Teresa Schantz wrote about the moment God made all of this crystal clear to her. As she was coming out of the grocery store she watched a little boy as he desperately tried carrying a big bag of ice, while attempting to make it look effortless. His father was doing the actual carrying, holding it with true ease by its handle.

The little boy cried out, "Don't let go, Dad. Now don't let go!"

The father replied, "I won't son. Is the bag too heavy? Is the ice too cold?"

"No no, Daddy! I've got it. But don't let go!"

As Teresa thought back on this scene it drew a significant parallel. She realized how like the little boy she was, hanging on tightly to her life, insisting on controlling it all by herself. She would go into the office early and do paperwork through lunch, obsessed with getting ahead and forcing her career to climb. Or how she would pick and choose the church activities that she wanted to participate in, those that most conveniently fit into her life. She was constantly planning for the future, making lists, structuring her priorities to meet her timelines. When, in reality, God was carrying the load and should have been controlling her life.[9]

She could have easily let go and allowed God to carry her burdens and rightfully rule her life. Instead, like Teresa, we too groan and moan and schedule yet one more task into an already overburdened schedule. The result is that we usually begin each day with immediate tension over the anticipation of the day's problems, stress and load.

Most of us don't even know what a balanced life would look like. Having grown up in the Catholic Church, I was taught by the Benedictine nuns in high school. St. Benedict envisioned a balanced life of prayer and work as the ideal one for his monastic communities. He believed that we should not be consumed with work or spend so much time in prayer that we neglect our other responsibilities. According to Benedict, it was all things in moderation: eating, drinking, sleeping, reading, working and praying.

As Sister Joan Chittister wrote in *Wisdom Distilled from the Daily*, in Benedict's Rule, "All must be given its due, but *only* its due." Did you know that when Benedict wrote his Rule, society was falling apart? It was during the Roman Empire, which was materially prosperous but as a society was in a state of decline. After Benedict's death, barbarian hordes would overrun Europe. The very survival of Western civilization was credited to Benedict with his message of balance and moderation, stability, hospitality and stewardship. In fact, this is why he was named the patron saint of Europe.

What's amazing about Benedict's approach is that it truly reflects God's way. The Benedictine monks lived a life that was balanced spiritually, physically and intellectually. For them, everyday, ordinary tasks had a spiritual aspect and their lives had routine and stability. Each person was also refreshed by having ordinary needs met. Sleep and rest had a proper place within their schedules.

THERE IS A RHYTHM TO A BALANCED LIFE

I think we have lost our rhythm for living. God designed the world with seasons and with order. Yet we attempt to live life without a basic core routine rhythm. The plants have a rhythm, animals have rhythm. How is it we think we can thrive by ignoring ours? My cats certainly are a constant reminder of the natural everyday routine rhythm for living. Miss Peony is like a clock. When 5:00 P.M. rolls around, whether I am finished with my work for the day or not, she persists with pawing and meowing until I leave my desk and follow her up the stairs. Her natural rhythm clock tells her it is the end of the work day. And unlike me, she actually hears and listens.

Perhaps this is why I am most peaceful at the beach. The natural rhythm of the ocean draws me in and regulates my day. I never wear a watch. I go to bed at dark and wake with the sunrise. I find the time to simply walk and talk with the Lord. As outdoors enthusiast Ad Crable wrote, "When I fall into the rhythm of the shore, I think of how I could do this for a long time. At the heart of it, I think, is the ocean, which for some reason prompts me to take stock of my life so far. I find myself pondering potential not realized and unfulfilled possibilities. Such low-tide thoughts are healthy, of course, and can lead the way to the mountaintops."[10]

To live a healthful life requires balance. Without it our lives will continue to run their chaotic path and we will continue to struggle.

SIMPLICITY MADE SIMPLE

Here are some thoughts to help you find the pathway to a simpler life journey:

As Cheryl Richardson wrote in her book, *Take Time for Your Life*, **SCHEDULE A PERSONAL DATE NIGHT**. For the next six months block out one afternoon or evening a week just for you. Spend this time doing something you really enjoy. Let work go and have fun. Get a massage, see a movie, or visit a museum. (My personal favorite is to get a massage!)

Do you want to enjoy more time with family and friends? Then it's time that you **LEARN HOW TO BE SPONTANEOUS**. Although this may seem like a contradiction, the simplest way to do this is to schedule "spontaneity breaks" into your day. This is a great way to keep your schedule from getting overbooked. Then you can use this planned break to grab your children and have a "shake the sillies out" song and dance!

GIVE YOURSELF PERMISSION TO DO NOTHING. This has been the hardest lesson for me to learn. Learning to shut off your mind is difficult but necessary. Some find meditation the easiest way to accomplish this. There are three types of basic meditation: (1) *Walking*—around your yard, around your home, wherever. Simply get up and walk; focus on your footsteps. Attempt to create a steady rhythm of five to ten seconds for each step. Sometimes repeating a prayer over and over is a good way to focus walking meditation. (2) *Mindfulness* meditation focuses on breathing. Sit comfortably in an upright position. Close your eyes and take three or four deep, slow breaths. Then breathe gently until you feel a sense of peace and calmness. Start with five-minute increments and build to fifteen. (3) *Ambient-sound* meditation involves the sounds around you. Instead of trying to tune them out, listen to them. It's akin to using white noise, like the sound of a fan, to lull you to sleep. Sit comfortably, close your eyes, relax your shoulders, breathe gently and pay attention to the sound around you. When I am attempting to nap in the greenroom, or lounge, at QVC, I use this technique to catch some rest. I purposely focus on the chatting of a particular person. I listen deeply to what is being said and this actually helps me to block out the lights and other noises and voices, allowing me to often fall asleep for a few minutes.

To lower stress, **MOVE AROUND**. Walk up a flight of stairs or do jumping jacks or anything that gets you moving. Stretching is another good stress releaser. Dawn Groves suggests some simple seated stretches that are great.[11] Start by lacing your fingers under one knee, and then draw your knee to your chest. Repeat with your other knee. Next, stretch your arms above your head, palms up and fingers interlaced. Drop your hands to your sides, then raise your right shoulder to your right ear, keeping your head vertical. Repeat with your left shoulder.

Living a healthful life requires a mind-body connection. Be sure to keep in touch with family and friends. **ESTABLISH A MEANINGFUL RELATIONSHIP** with someone who lives near you. Keep a positive attitude toward living. Those that have lived the longest have an optimistic approach to life's setbacks. They have developed coping skills that help them more easily weather life's stresses such as death and divorce. You always have a choice. You can either let the bad things that happen to you make you miserable, or you can choose to let them make you even better!

> **Lord, help me to let You be in control and order my days.**
> **Help me to choose wisely and to remember**
> **to leave room for the daily rhythm of Your design.**
> **Help me Lord to accomplish all that You want**
> **me to achieve this day and to leave the rest**
> **of the work for another place and time.**

Work and Life

For even when we were with you, this we commanded

you, that if any would not work, neither should he eat.

—2 THESSALONIANS 3:10 (KJV)

A dictionary definition of *work* calls it an effort exerted in some purposeful activity, such as one's occupation. Even God is depicted in Genesis 1 as doing work and finding satisfaction in it when He created the world. God gave Adam meaningful work in the garden before the fall. And here in 2 Thessalonians, Paul calls on Christians to earn their own living by working.

Different Hebrew words define the various types of labor. I especially like the Hebrew word *àbad* because it portrays work as accomplishment that brings satisfaction or significant service.[12] This kind of work not only yields appropriate monetary reward but is also fulfilling for the person who does it.

As discussed in the previous chapter, a healthful life requires balance. And work certainly is a large part of our lives. All of us must learn to find the balance between leisure and laziness, and working and being a workaholic. Just as relaxation and recreation provide a necessary and much-needed balance in our lives, so too does work. As Christians, we are to be responsible and make the most of the talents and time. We have to provide for ourselves and our dependents, and to share with those less fortunate. Just as St. Benedict said, we ought to rest when we need rest and work when we should be working.

It can be difficult to find that balance. Many of us, especially Americans, struggle with long work weeks and a work ethic best described as workaholism. Did you know that in some parts of Europe it's unusual to work more than thirty-five hours per week? Americans work as much as sixty hours a week. And that doesn't include the work we take home with us. I wonder how many of us are finding the kind of satisfaction portrayed in the word *àbad* in all those hours of work? I personally believe that if we follow the passions God has instilled in us, we will find the most satisfying work. Yet there are experts who believe that work is just work, and your life should be found elsewhere. How sad is that—that you would spend half your life working and not enjoy it?

Sometimes guidance for a new and different way of working comes from the simplest phrases. For Jim Hosett, a single man, work *was* a significant part of his life. He considered his co-workers his family. Imagine his dismay when he was told that after thirty-three years of employment at the same company that it was closing due to bankruptcy. At fifty-eight years of age, he would find himself without a job. To make matters worse, that very same day his stepsister called to say his father had had a stroke and wasn't doing well. She asked Jim to come see him.

On Saturday morning Jim boarded a plane to his dad's house in West Virginia. When it came time for his dad's medication, Jim went to get it and grabbed a ripe red apple from the counter as well. On a whim, he cut it up, arranged the slices on a plate and carried the snack to his dad. The strangest expression crossed his face. For a second, Jim thought he had done something wrong. His dad looked as though he was going to cry. "Dad? What's the matter?" he asked. "Nobody's cut me an apple like that since my wife died," he said, squeezing Jim's hand. "It's just like she used to do." A lump formed in Jim's throat. He was amazed that such a small gesture would make his dad so happy. Back at work, a fellow manager suggested Jim become a consultant because he could do well at it. But Jim was struggling with whether he wanted to do *well*, or do something *more*. It wasn't about money or prestige. It was about that feeling he had gotten helping his dad. Jim spoke with his dad every day on the phone. One day after talking for more than an hour, his dad suddenly said, "God has more in store for you, Jim. Trust Him."

Those simple words eventually encouraged Jim to seek employment at an assisted living facility. Even with his many years of executive experience, he took a job as a nurse's assistant. It has turned out to be a perfect fit. Jim feels connected and needed as he empties ice buckets and collects laundry. He loves learning about the residents' lives, their hopes, their fears and their prayers. And he tells them that God isn't through with them yet either. He never is.

As more and more folks work into and through their retirement years, a second career may be the opportunity for the most fulfilling kind of job. But that doesn't mean you have to wait until then to enjoy your work. I started out in chemical engineering because I was good at it—not because I loved it. After five years, I quit and went back to school to get my interior design degree. In spite of the fact that I probably would have earned more money as an engineer, I have never regretted that decision. I love my work.

THERE IS MORE TO COME

If you are struggling with your job and wish you could simply change careers, consider evaluating your lifestyle to see if it's possible. Most of the time, we feel chained to a job because we believe we cannot afford to quit. Ask yourself what you would do if you found out tomorrow that your salary was being cut in half? You certainly would find a way to rein in expenses. Perhaps you would even consider renting out a room in your home. What if you did some of those cost-cutting things now, even though you don't have to? That could give you the freedom to look for a more emotionally rewarding position.

Thousands of American workers are cutting back on hours or changing careers as they search to find a better balance between work and life. And a full eighty percent of boomers say they intend to work even after retirement, according to a Yankelovich poll. "This generation idealizes work," believes J. Walker Smith, president of Yankelovich, who says, "Meaningful work was a baby-boomer concept."

S I M P L I C I T Y   M A D E   S I M P L E

Here are some ideas to help you improve the job you have and learn how to benefit from a balanced work-life situation:

If you are regularly bringing home work from the office, you are robbing yourself of your life! Experiment with **LEAVING YOUR WORK AT THE OFFICE** for two nights a week and see how things go. Then you can take another night or two off as you learn to work smarter rather than harder or longer.

Remember, you don't have to make big changes all at once. If you are currently working nearly sixty hours a week, start with the realization that it is possible to be happy and productive working less. How about trying a forty-hour workweek? **LOOK AT YOUR SCHEDULE** and start making the necessary changes so you can work less. If you've always gone in an hour earlier than required, start using that time to either catch a few z's or catch up on your physical fitness. If you always stay late, apply the same rules as above.

Carefully **ANALYZE YOUR WORK PATTERN.** Something is wrong if you're unable to complete the work you feel you must get done during regular business hours. Do you allow co-workers to interrupt you on a regular basis? If so, then try setting aside two half-hour blocks throughout the day as the only time you will accept visitors. Think about how much time you spend on the telephone that could more efficiently be handled with a quick e-mail. Another time waster is disorganization. Hiring a professional efficiency consultant or organizer may save you hours weekly.

DELEGATE whenever possible. Some people simply try to do too much or have never learned how to delegate. Many people are afraid that if they delegate, the job won't be done satisfactorily. To give you and the other person confidence in getting the job done well, be sure he or she has all the information needed to make good decisions. Assign work to those who have the best experience and delegate only to qualified individuals. Make sure they clearly understand what is expected. Don't forget to check with them halfway through to completion to be sure all is proceeding on target. In addition, be accessible for questions and guidance. And always acknowledge a job well done.

THINK ABOUT YOUR HOME LIFE. Are you avoiding someone or something and using work as an excuse not to come home? Sometimes there can be an ulterior motive for working long hours or staying away from home. If so, it's time to take responsibility and start making positive changes in your work life.

How much time do you spend commuting? **CONSIDER PUBLIC TRANSPORTATION** if it's more than thirty minutes each way. You will be amazed at how much you can accomplish on the train ride to work if you don't have to do the driving.

TAKE A VACATION! God's plan for a balanced life requires rest for rejuvenation. In a 2000 study of 12,338 middle-aged men at risk for heart disease, researchers at the State University of New York in Oswego found that those who did not take regular vacations were more likely to die, especially from heart problems, over a nine-year period than those who took time off. They wrote: "Several smaller workplace studies confirm the short-term benefits. People tend to sleep better after more than a week off, have fewer physical complaints than they did before the break, and report being more optimistic and energetic than they were before." Researcher Elaine Eaker found that middle-aged women who took vacations very infrequently (defined as once every six years or less often) had eight times the risk of either having a heart attack or dying of heart disease.

> Lord, I realize that any accomplishment worth achieving
> will come by Your grace and not by works.
> Please guide me to a life balanced between work and
> rest, service and relaxation. Bless the work of my hands
> to accomplish more in less time, and bless the peace
> of my mind when I am resting in Your promises.

Nurture Your Mind

A wise man will hear, and will increase learning; and a
man of understanding shall attain unto wise counsels.

—PROVERBS 1:5 (KJV)

We all know that Solomon was a wise man, but I think what makes him exceptionally wise is that when God said He would give him anything he wanted, he was smart enough to ask for wisdom. I also find it interesting that God was so pleased with this request that He also gave him great riches, power and peace.

Being "book smart" is not the same thing as being wise. Wisdom is much more; it is a basic attitude that affects every aspect of life. And the first step to wisdom is to fear the Lord, to honor and respect Him and to live in awe of His almighty power. It is our faith in God that is the foundation for understanding, having a right attitude and how we should act. By trusting in God, we allow Him to make us truly wise.

Living in the information age, we certainly are not lacking for knowledge. It is plentiful. Yet without wisdom, information and knowledge are worthless. Just search the Internet and you can find far more information than you need. Unfortunately, it will take a lot of wisdom to discern what is true and what is not. I liken our information age to Proverbs 1:20 (KJV) that says, "Wisdom crieth without; she uttereth her voice in the streets." I can just picture wisdom shouting to us in the streets. This figurative illustration is used to make wisdom come alive for us. Wisdom is not a separate being; it is the mind of God revealed, which means God is making His wisdom available to all of us. We just have to reach out and grab it.

However, for God's wisdom to be useful, we need understanding. And that requires a healthy brain to process the wisdom that is available to us. All the experts agree that by learning something new we can improve brain function. And some doctors now believe it is possible to build a "cognitive reserve" (developing strength in other parts of the brain) that enables a person to avoid dementia in old age. Only God could create a system that repairs itself through repeated use!

Neurologist Jay Lombard, coauthor of *Balance Your Brain, Balance Your Life*, says, "We used to think that the adult brain couldn't grow. Now we know that it not only grows but also regenerates old cells that are out of use."[13] Although age is an undeniable factor, we can encourage brain growth by taking some simple steps to strengthen and challenge our abilities. Just like our muscles, our brains need exercise in order to function at their best.

BALANCE IS TAKING TIME TO PLAY

One of the simplest and most enjoyable things you can do to help your brain is to play games, such as chess, checkers, backgammon, cards or word games like Scrabble. These kinds of activities force you to think ahead and look at the big picture. As you ponder your options, you are exercising your brain's muscle. In a study published by the Albert Einstein College of Medicine, Bronx, New York, that looked at nearly five hundred elderly people over a twenty-one-year period, researchers found that those who played games at least once a week cut their risk of developing dementia by at least half. And the benefits increased with the number of times they played. That is because these kinds of activities require left-brain logic and the ability to think things through before acting.

Get out your joysticks and start your engines! Believe it or not, Nintendo, pinball and juggling are all excellent right-brain activities because they force you to act on instinct. It turns out these are the perfect right-brain kinds of activities. Other right-brain exercises include looking at art, listening to music, and doodling. These are classic ways to tease the abstract right side of your brain. Songs that relax and activate parts of the brain's frontal lobes and limbic areas on both the right and the left sides bring the two halves of your brain into harmony.

Hobbies are another great way to increase your brainpower. Did you know that Albert Einstein played violin and Luciano Pavarotti is a soccer fanatic? These kinds of passionate pursuits help the mind escape and expand. Research shows that pleasure is a crucial component for a healthy brain. Needlework is a hobby that many of us find relaxing but it is accomplishing more than relaxation. By cultivating fine motor skills through needlework or playing an instrument, we are establishing new circuits throughout the brain.

Neurologist Richard Restak suggests picking something you enjoy and doing it. All my life, I wanted to learn to sing. When I turned forty-four, I started voice lessons. Not that I ever expect to sing in public. This was just for my brain and me!

Some activities are good for body and brain. A simple way to turn a heart-healthy workout into a brain lifter is to add music. A team at Ohio State University had thirty-three cardiac patients exercise while listening to music. After exercising with music, the patients did twice as well on a test of cognitive ability as they had done after exercising in silence. Dr. Charles Emery, PhD, suggests that exercise alone causes positive changes in the nervous system and by adding music we may be stimulating different pathways in the brain.

All of this information simply confirms what we already knew—a balanced life is the best therapy for body, soul and brain!

SIMPLICITY MADE SIMPLE

Here are some ideas you can try in order to encourage your brain into a smarter way of functioning:

BE ACTIVE. Exercise increases your brainpower. As Stan Colcombe, PhD, at Beckman Institute for Advanced Studies says, "The greater your level of fitness, the less brain tissue you will lose as you age."

Aerobic exercise will pump more blood and oxygen to your brain. But it also can have a positive effect on the intracellular messenger called brain drive neurotropin factor (BDNF). This has shown to slow the rate of brain-cell death and increase the production of new brain cells. Simply by taking a **FIFTEEN-MINUTE *BRISK* WALK** that elevates your heart rate, three times a week, you can get some much-needed exercise for your brain.

REDUCE STRESS. You've heard it before—but now we have yet another reason to reduce the stress in our lives—our brains. Stress produces a hormone called cortisol that starves your brain of fuel, particularly in the hippocampus, where memories are stored and retrieved. Scientists have found that chronic cortisol elevation kills brain cells and shrinks our brains.

Grab your pencils and let's **DO A CROSSWORD PUZZLE**! Who knew that one of my favorite pastimes could be so good for me? But it's true, working crossword puzzles is like taking your brain out for a good run. Will Shortz, crossword editor for *The New York Times*, gives the following suggestions for beginners: Start by scanning the clues and answer those you know. Next, tackle the fill-in-the-blank and the shorter clues. Be aware that vowel-heavy words like *iota*, *eel*, and *Oreo* are used often in puzzles, as are celebrity or famous names like *Uma* and *Agee*.

As we age, we all wonder what happened to our memory. I love the T-shirt that Kim Komando, computer guru, sells—on the front it says, "Out of Memory!" We all start to notice a decline in memory around forty years of age. Experts recommend **USING THE TECHNIQUE OF *CHUNKING*** or clustering to learn. For example, learn a credit-card number in chunks of three digits. Others suggest mnemonic techniques for remembering names. This is when you make an association such as an Easter hat with lilies on the head of a woman you've just met whose name is Lily. However, when I interviewed a memory expert about the fact that I have never been able to remember names, he said, "Then you never will. Don't worry about it." That made me feel so much better. All experts do agree that a key element to memory is emotional content. That's why a song that once elicited a strong feeling can also spark memories of an earlier time in our lives.

Just like the rest of our bodies, **OUR BRAINS NEED A HEALTHY DIET**. Research shows that eating fish, especially cold-water species such as salmon, tuna and mackerel are best because they contain omega-3 fatty acids in abundance. These acids help reduce inflammation and protect brain cells from free radical damage.

Did you know that **DEPRESSION** can affect your short-term memory? It's true. Depression causes you to lose your ability to focus and concentrate, and that directly influences your ability to store new memories. If you are struggling with depression, do seek professional help.

Father, help me to grow in wisdom, knowledge,
and understanding of Your ways and Your purpose
for my life. I will keep music in my heart
and sing praises of Your good work in my life.

Set the Goal

Being confident of this very thing, that he
which hath begun a good work in you
will perform it until the day of Jesus Christ.

—PHILIPPIANS 1:6 (KJV)

If you have ever struggled with confidence in any area of your life, this verse from Philippians is for you. Whether you struggle for lack of progress in your spiritual life or your personal life, know that God never leaves a project unfinished. He began a good work in you and promises to continue until the finish. Just as He did for the Philippians, God will help you.

We can be encouraged because of the knowledge that God will not give up on us. When we feel inadequate or distressed, we can remember God's promise of provision. We should never let our present situation or condition rob us of the joy of knowing Christ or keep us from growing. Having the confidence to know that God is always with us, working in us and helping us is a key element to reaching our goals and dreams.

God is the giver of dreams; He has plans for us. And He will give us the ability to accomplish those plans, no matter what. The Bible is filled with people who felt unworthy or unfit for the plans and goals that God assigned to them. Yet each one that chose to allow God to work His plan in his or her life succeeded abundantly.

Even as Paul encouraged the Philippians to press on toward the goal for the prize of the upward call of God (see Philippians 3:14, NKJV) so, too, should we seek to follow Paul's advice and strive to be the best we can be. Paul also encouraged the Philippians to forget the past including their failures and mistakes. Those who are mature in their spiritual walk press on in faith knowing that God will reveal His plan. They accommodate for their inadequacy by trusting in Him.

Clearly we are to work with confidence toward the goal. But unless we actually have a defined goal, we can have no clear direction or purpose for our lives. We may be full of confidence, but where are we going? The wonderful thing about goals is that they can be applied to any area of life: spiritual, mental, social, financial or physical. The key is to make and set goals so we know where we are going. After all, we cannot even ask for directions if we don't know the destination.

The greatest gift my mother ever gave me was telling me that whatever I wanted to do in life, I could learn. That simple phrase has been a foundation for courage in pursuing what others may have thought silly or unrealistic dreams in my life. I have also been blessed with a "dreamer" husband. He dreams big wonderful dreams. And he believes they are possible realities. As a result, he believes that I can do amazing things. Guess what? With his encouragement and faith, and God's grace, I am doing (and have done) far more than I could ever have imagined on my own!

As Og Mandino, author of the classic motivational book *The Greatest Salesman in the World*, says, "The easiest thing to find on God's green earth is someone to tell you all the things you *cannot* do."[14] Mandino encourages us to give our dreams a chance to come true by avoiding the naysayers of the world. And that includes freeing ourselves by saying, "I can," rather than "I can't." Consider how many opportunities you may have missed over the last five or ten years simply because you said, "I can't." Many of us defeat ourselves before we even get started by thinking it will be too hard or not be probable. Nothing in life worth achieving is easy. But if God gives you a goal or a dream, who are you to question His authority? We will never know what we can accomplish unless we try. Mandino also says, "He who cherishes a beautiful vision, a lofty ideal in his heart, will one day realize it. Just as an oak tree sleeps in an acorn, so in the highest vision of the soul a waking angel stirs. Dreams are the seedlings of realities."[15]

SET CLEAR GOALS

Goal setting is a process that gives us direction for our lives. If we set goals and move step-by-step toward achieving them, we will succeed. But we must know precisely what we want to achieve first. That is why it is necessary to set clearly defined goals that can be measured as we progress. By seeing forward progress we will not be discouraged. Therefore, our goals must walk that fine line between too small and too lofty. If they are so lofty that they are unattainable and cannot be mapped out in achievable steps, then we are setting ourselves up for disappointment and failure. Moving forward with your goals, step-by-step, will raise your self-confidence as you realize your competency with each accomplishment.

All high achievers use goal setting as a standard technique for success. Athletes, successful businesspeople and everyday great moms and dads all set goals for both short- and long-term motivation. Goal setting helps us to focus our areas of education and organize our resources. Goal setting can be broken down into different levels. Decide first what you want to do with your life on a large scale. For example, family, education, financial and career accomplishments would be considered large-scale goals. Second, break down these goals into smaller steps that will ultimately lead to reaching your lifetime goals. It is only once you have these steps in place that you can begin working toward achievement.

Most experts will tell you to set time goals to match your achievement goals. For example, you may want to set a goal to take a weeklong cruise to Alaska. The time frame for this might be two years. In order to accomplish this goal, you will need marker time frames to judge how well you are coming along with the finances for this dream. By setting six-month minigoals and reevaluating at each six-month increment, you will be able to manage and ultimately attain your dream. This same kind of time measurement should be used for all your goals. It is also a good idea to periodically review your longer-term plans, and modify them to reflect your changing needs or priorities.

You can never be too young or too old to have dreams. Goals and dreams are not only appropriate for all but they are necessary. When we lose our hope for a better tomorrow, we lose faith. Without faith, we are lost. Your thoughts and your dreams are your greatest gifts.

SIMPLICITY MADE SIMPLE

Here are some words of encouragement as you take courage, have faith and follow your dreams:

Declare war on your negative feelings. Don't let them win the battle in your mind. Resolve to **END ALL NEGATIVE SELF-TALK** and focus on the positive.

WRITE YOUR GOALS DOWN ON PAPER. Keeping them in your head is never as effective as writing them down. Make a contract with yourself and sign and date it. Then remember to review your progress according to the time-frame markers you have set.

AMBITIOUS YET OBTAINABLE GOALS are best. Setting easy goals is like cheating. They will have little meaning. Impossible goals are also a foolproof way to avoid success. The best goals are those that stretch us to do our best.

HAVE AN ACTION PLAN. I recently decided that I wanted to lose ten pounds. Believe me, I could talk about losing ten pounds forever but unless I put a plan together to accomplish that goal it would never happen. It has been four weeks as of this writing, and I have lost nearly five pounds. How did I do this? I simply put together a healthful plan for eating that eliminated sugars, breads and packaged foods. Then I prepared menus and shopping lists to help me stay true to my new way of eating. These were the little steps that will ultimately help me accomplish my goal.

GOALS MUST BE SPECIFIC and measurable. If you want to improve your spiritual walk, then set a well-defined goal to accomplish it. You may, for example, organize a Bible study group as one way of making progress.

SET PRIORITIES. If you have several goals, give each a priority. This will help you avoid feeling overwhelmed by too many goals. It will also help to direct your attention to your most important goals.

Failure to meet your goals doesn't matter as long as you learn something. Then use those lessons to help make your goal-setting program better. For example, if you realized that part of the failure was due to a deficit in your skills, then you may want to take a class on that particular skill. Perhaps you failed because you didn't give yourself a realistic time frame for success. **MAKE ADJUSTMENTS** for future goals that are more realistic.

Remember that your goals may change as you mature. It is always a good idea to **REGULARLY REFLECT ON YOUR PERSONAL GROWTH** and your personality. Sometimes our priorities change and what seemed important five years ago is no longer relevant.

Ultimately, goal setting will help you **DECIDE WHAT IS IMPORTANT** for you to achieve in your life by separating the significant from the irrelevant. A goal can help motivate you to achieve more than you thought you could. And that achievement will build your self-confidence and your faith in God as your partner in life.

Lord, I want to finish the course that You have planned for my life. Give me a clear vision of what I should be doing in the future so that I can prepare for it now. I will keep my trust in You, knowing that You will direct my path.

PART THREE

The Greatest of All Is Love

THE WAY TO NURTURE healthy emotions is to understand that life is about people, not things. It is possible to view life through an attitude of gratitude, and consequently learn to find pleasure in simple things we have long ignored. In this section, I will discuss how developing Christlike attitudes of humility and genuine love for others keeps us healthy and full of joyous anticipation for each new day.

Nurture an Attitude
of Gratitude

In every thing give thanks: for this is the will
of God in Christ Jesus concerning you.

—1 THESSALONIANS 5:18 (KJV)

I f the *will* of God is for us to be thankful in all things, then why is it that most of us manage to ignore this command almost daily? The apostle Paul was not teaching the Thessalonians to thank God *for* everything, but to give thanks *in* everything. Perhaps this is where we get tripped up. Of course God doesn't want us to thank Him for the bad things that happen. But we can be thankful in the midst of difficult circumstances for Who God is and for the good He can bring even during tough times. Being thankful is a matter of attitude.

As Hal Urban, author of *Life's Greatest Lessons*[16] wrote, "Being thankful is a habit—the best one you'll ever have." Urban teaches a class on thankfulness with a forty-eight-hour experiment. It goes like this. First he challenges his class to attempt not to complain for a twenty-four hour period. If they do complain during that time, they are to write down their complaint and continue with the test. Out of all the years that Urban has given this assignment, which now includes more than seventy thousand people, only four have managed not to complain! Pretty amazing results, aren't they?

His lesson continues as he prompts the class to tell him what they learned through this twenty-four-hour period. All of the students answered that they all complain too much, and that most of their complaints were puny. Next Urban asks them to make a list consisting of three columns of what they appreciate in life and categorize them as "things," "people" and "other." The students were able to list all the material things they appreciate, and all the people they appreciate. But when they got to the "other" column they were confused. At Urban's prompting, they began to brainstorm topics for the final label. They came up with a great list of options such as freedom, opportunity, friendship, love, God, faith, security and intelligence.

Part three of the assignment required the student to read these lists four times over the next twenty-four hours. The next day it was obvious by body language alone that a transformation had taken place. When he asked them if they felt any different than they had before the experiment, their answers were obvious by the big smiles on their faces. As Urban says, "Thankfulness does wonders for the soul." He teaches this class to high school and college students. He has discovered that the results are even more dramatic with adults. The reality is that adults complain more than youngsters do. Perhaps it's because we are more entrenched in the habit of complaining and we've been taking things for granted for a much longer time.

It's amazing how we can change our attitude simply by changing our perspective. And thankfulness is a perspective of life that can be learned. It's the old story of whether the glass is half empty or half full. We automatically become more fulfilled by appreciating what we have and seeing opportunities as half full rather than half empty. It's sad that with all the blessings we have, we can still find things to complain about. As Ruth Stafford Peale said, "Live one day without any unhealthy thoughts. It may be very difficult, but try another day until it becomes habitual, and life will move in the direction of becoming healthy, vital and alive." Aside from adopting an attitude of gratitude we can also spread that message to all those we encounter in our daily lives.

Rick Hamlin, an editor at *Guideposts* magazine, recounted his experience at work when his boss asked him to write down the names of all the people there who had helped him with his job. For a year he had been in charge of the fillers and shorts at the magazine, all those one-line quotes and brief anecdotes that fit at the bottom of the page. He was frustrated because it was taking the better part of two days to look back through his files for twelve issues, recording who had found each item. He thought what an incalculable waste of time, when he could be doing a lot more productive things. But as the list of names grew, he was astonished at how many people had helped him that past year. As he typed the information he was amazed at how what had seemed to be so odious now filled him with appreciation. He never realized how much help he had received from his colleagues. In fact, he was deeply indebted to them and realized he could not have done the job without them. After finishing the list, his boss said, "Great. Now I want you to pass it around the office with some explanation." It was the easiest memo Hamlin ever wrote. And the consequences were even more amazing as more contributions flooded his in-box. As his boss said, "You can never go wrong with appreciation."

SMILE AT SOMEONE TODAY

I guess that just shows that when we are grateful for what we have, God may bless us with more. Sometimes the most seemingly mundane things turn out to be significant inspiration for positive change. A smile from a stranger can change your attitude for an entire day. Before you know it, you too are smiling and that smile gets passed along to the next person. Who knows how many people's lives are affected.

By contrast, imagine the negativity that can be passed around a community by a road-rage infected driver. Each person that he encounters is subjected to his anger and before you know it there are a lot of angry people on the road. Let's hope that as we realize the major role gratefulness plays in our happiness, the more attention we will give to having an attitude of gratitude. After all, it's hard to complain about what we don't have if we are focused on what we do have.

In the end, we should keep our focus on God and His abundant blessings in our lives. As Benedictine monk David Steindl-Rast says, "Gratefulness is more than a momentary emotion. It's a profoundly spiritual and powerfully healing state of being that can reverse the 'downward spiral of desperation' and create an upward, ever-expanding spiral that brings greater and greater happiness."

SIMPLICITY MADE SIMPLE

Here are some grateful ideas to help you adopt the right attitude:

START YOUR DAY BY THANKING GOD for the fact that you are alive! Starting your day with a prayer of gratitude will put you in a good mood for the rest of the day.

END EACH DAY BY THANKING GOD for a specific event that occurred that day for which you feel grateful.

USE GRATITUDE to ward off jealousy and negativity. In turn, you will feel better about yourself. Feeling positive about yourself will give you more confidence, and that can lead to nothing but success.

There will always be others who are better off than you. Whether they are better educated or have more shouldn't matter. Instead, always **GIVE THANKS** for the plenty or little you do have, knowing there is also always someone worse off than you are.

Gratitude is good for the soul because it shifts our focus from worry and self-absorption to what is truly important. **TRY KEEPING A GRATITUDE JOURNAL.** Incorporate it into your regular prayer time. Then revisit the pages at the end of each quarter of the year. You will be amazed at the blessings you will find in your life.

Consider trying Hal Urban's forty-eight-hour experiment. **STOP COMPLAINING** and then make lists of all the things you have to be grateful for. This can be enough to change your perspective and immediately improve the quality of your life.

Make a conscious effort to **THANK SOMEONE EVERY DAY**, even if it's just for the little things they do for you. Make the thank-you personal by handwriting a note and mailing it. Get yourself some stationery or postcards and proper postage. Avoid using the pre-inscribed "Thank You" note cards. Store all these items where they are easily accessible so you will have no excuses for neglecting to send a proper thank-you.

Lord, I am grateful for the uncountable blessings
that You have given me. I realize that there are many
things that You do of which I am not even aware.
Forgive me for my selfish perspective of life,
and bring to my attention the good in others.

Family, Friends and Love

For if they fall, the one will lift up his fellow:

but woe to him that is alone when he falleth;

for he hath not another to help him up.

—ECCLESIASTES 4:10 (KJV)

It is clear from this verse that God designed us for community. God seeks to have a relationship with us, and that is the best model we could have for all of our relationships. Relationships are at the center of who we are because of Who God is in the Trinity. As with all good things, relationships can be the most fulfilling part of our lives, but they can also be the most frustrating. Why? Because relationships by their very nature engage our emotions at the deepest level. We were designed to be part of a community; without relationships our souls suffer from the absence of the very purpose of our existence.

Our most important relationships should start with our family. As the adage goes, we can't choose family, only friends, which speaks to the reality of how easily family relationships can rub us the wrong way. Even with their conflicts, there is an aspect of family relationships that can rarely be duplicated. My five siblings and I have certainly had our share of disagreements and differences of opinion. Nonetheless, we all know that when push comes to shove, we can count on each other to be there. When our father was living his last few months on earth, hospital and social workers were amazed at how easily we organized our team of family to care for and nurture Dad. Each of us knew ourselves well enough that it was simple for us to decide on who would be responsible for what. Dad's journey home was truly peaceful as well as joyfully bittersweet. Dad was so relieved that he was finally able to give up the fight and totally enjoy the love of his family as he awaited his journey home.

Friendship is the second most important kind of relationship we can have. At my father's funeral I realized that each member of our family had been supported by a lifelong friend throughout this difficult time. What a blessing that was for each one of us. Family relationships give us a sense of belonging and heritage, while friendships provide the much-needed context for life that only a peer can give.

A friend's husband phoned me once to thank me for being a friend to his wife. He said it had so positively affected their relationship because by her sharing with me the difficulties she was experiencing in her marriage, she realized that she was not alone. Many of the issues she was struggling with were issues through which we all struggle. I think this is why being part of a small group or life group at a church is so important and healthy. We learn from each other as we share life's challenges, blessings and successes, and simply live life together.

WE CAN BUILD HEALTHY RELATIONSHIPS

Conflict is as old as life itself. Satan was there in Eden, and he is still here today. He so easily engages us into self-minded destructive thoughts that fog our hearts and cause us to speak unfortunate words. As James 1:2 tells us, we are to consider it all joy when we encounter various trials. It is clear that trials will come even in the best of relationships. Proverbs 2:2 makes it clear that we are to make our ears attentive to wisdom. However, it's pretty hard to hear wisdom if we are doing all of the talking or shouting! A defensive attitude will not be a good road to resolution or peace. The moment we take a defensive tone, we have already escalated the situation.

Many of us simply do not know how to fight fair. Name-calling and dragging up old offenses and previous errors that should have been forgiven by now should never be part of an argument. Yet think how easily we can procure that list of every wrong we have ever endured. It's sad to watch adults continue to live and relive the hurts of the distant past. Instead of moving forward and learning from those experiences, they use them as excuses for their own continued bad behavior. Ephesians 4:26 (KJV) says, "Be ye angry, and sin not: let not the sun go down upon your wrath." This tells us that it is important to handle our anger properly. If it is thoughtlessly vented, it can hurt others and destroy relationships. If left to bottle up and fester inside, it can cause us to become bitter and destroy us from within. Paul tells us to deal with our anger immediately in a way that *builds* relationships rather than destroys them. Probably the thing I find most frustrating for myself is the reality that I continue to make the same kinds of mistakes over and over again. Intellectually, I know better. I have read and studied all the right ways to deal with conflicts and anger, yet my old ingrained wrong-way patterns sneak back up in the heat of an emotional upset. It's especially disheartening when I find myself reacting to my husband in the same way I reacted to someone from my past. It happens because the situation drags up old feelings that are similar to the way I am feeling now.

The old way of responding simply takes over by force of habit. Sometimes I wonder if I will ever learn. Awareness, they say, is half the battle. So I am hopeful that someday I will rein in those bad habits and act like the mature woman my age says I am.

Of all the things that you can do to maintain your most important relationships, the best is simply spending time with those you love.

SIMPLICITY MADE SIMPLE

Here are some thoughts to inspire you to deepen your ties with family and friends:

New research from the University of Minnesota Medical School's Center for Adolescent Health and Development found that sharing family meals makes healthier kids—even for families that don't have the best relationships. Try scheduling three **FAMILY MEALS** a week that everyone agrees not to miss. The most important element of the dinner ritual is catching up and sharing bits and pieces from the day. Children who eat dinner with their families are less likely to smoke, use drugs or abuse alcohol, says a study from the National Center on Addiction and Substance Abuse.

KIDS LIKE THINGS SIMPLE. Instead of planning activities for you and your children—ask them what they would like to do. You may be surprised to find that they would much rather spend time doing something fun like tossing a baseball than going to yet another expensive, crowded theme park.

GRANDPARENTS can create the most memorable moments. Finance writer Jeff Opdyke wrote in his column in the *Wall Street Journal* that his best memories were those of nodding off in his grandfather's old, brown pickup truck on his way to a day of fishing. He also fondly remembers drinking Chocolate Soldier and learning how to clean bass and catfish on an aging wooden table in the backyard. Opdyke says, "Those memories didn't cost my grandparents any significant sum of money, yet three decades later they define exactly the kind of happiness I hope my son one day associates with his own childhood. That's the definition of priceless."

BE GOOD TO YOUR SPOUSE. Simply giving your spouse fifteen minutes a day for checking in can help you unwind and provide a positive environment.

SPONTANEITY can be an opportunity for some of our best memories. *Guideposts* writer Shari Smyth tells of an especially memorable time when she and her husband took a spontaneous ride on a Ferris wheel when they found themselves at the site of a carnival in the midst of their day of errands. As they laughingly climbed aboard the red flimsy seat that was rocking crazily, her stomach lurched. The attendant closed the thin steel bar and her husband asked, "Do you feel safe?" as he put his arm around her shoulder. "I do now," she said, leaning up against him. The years melted away into a magical moment that ended with an "I love you kiss." Seize the opportunity to create memorable moments in your life.

When it comes to conflicts—having a plan in advance is the best remedy. It's easy to get off balance and feel as though you don't know how to resolve the conflict. **SEEK FIRST TO UNDERSTAND**—before telling your side of the story, listen to the complete story from the other side. Don't get sidetracked—be sure you can actually name what you are fighting about. If not, then it probably isn't worth the fight. Or perhaps it's just one of those days when you were feeling particularly sensitive or vulnerable. In that case, the best advice I can give you is to simply learn to say "I'm sorry." Examine your own heart before casting stones. Things always go better and easier when we turn to God *first* rather than later. Pray that God will show you the error of your ways and take your focus off those with whom you are arguing. Pursue resolution and then seek forgiveness. Then allow God's soothing touch to heal the inevitable wounds of the heart.

Lord, I confess that I have old relational habits that
neither bless the people in my life, nor satisfy my own
longing to connect with others. Please cleanse me
of emotional reactions that do not glorify You. Create in
me a heart that feels situations as You feel them,
and help me to love other people as You do.

Pride, Rage, Bitterness, Oh No!

Do nothing out of selfish ambition or vain conceit,

but in humility consider others better than yourselves.

Each of you should look not only to your own interests,

but also to the interests of others.

—PHILIPPIANS 2:3–4 (NIV)

Philippi was a very cosmopolitan city. With so many different backgrounds among its church members, unity certainly was an issue. There is no evidence of widespread division in the church; nonetheless, this verse from Paul indicates a need to safeguard the church's unity. Paul warned the church members to guard against any selfishness, prejudice or jealousy that might lead to dissension. He encouraged them to show genuine interest in others as a positive step toward maintaining unity among the believers.

When I first did the outline for this book, I separated the negative emotions like rage, pride, self-centeredness and bitterness from the positive ones such as humility, forgiveness and self-control. But as I began to research and write, I realized they belonged together because they are the "opposites" of each other. If we can learn to execute the positive attributes, we probably won't have to worry about the negative ones! Paul confirmed this in his instructions above. If we take the positive step forward by showing sincere interest in others, we'll be too busy to focus on our own fragile egos.

I love the story Guideposts writer Oscar Greene tells about his lesson of humility. Oscar was selected to learn the new automatic boring mill at his company that produces machine parts.

He was very excited about the opportunity to learn a new craft. For seven weeks, he watched, learned and operated the mill. Finally, one Monday morning it was his turn to demonstrate the magic of the new mill. With his co-workers gathered, Oscar, thinking he knew it all by now, pressed the start button . . . and nothing happened. His co-workers giggled, and one said, "Maybe it's out of gas. Have you put a nickel in it?" Oscar blushed.

For hours, their chief electrician tried to solve the problem without success. They called the manufacturer, and within hours a youthful expert arrived. He smiled, pressed the start button and the machine roared into action. He turned the machine on and off several times, and then said, "I think I know your problem." With his left hand, he reached under a cover and pushed two matchsticklike switches in opposite directions. Then he pressed the start button. "These are safety switches," he said. "They must be reversed, or the machine won't start." Never during Oscar's seven weeks of training had he seen the instructor touch those switches. Oscar went on to teach others to use the machine. But he never forgot God's lesson. Oscar said, "Those two little switches moved me from pride to humiliation to humility. And in doing so, they made me a better teacher."

Matthew 18:4 (NAS) says, "Whoever then humbles himself as this child, he is the greatest in the kingdom of heaven." Being humble means having a true perspective of ourselves. It is not about putting ourselves down; that can lead to false humility. In God's eyes, we all are sinners saved only by grace. The good news is that we are saved and therefore have great worth in God's kingdom. God's way says we are to lay aside selfishness and treat others with respect and courtesy. Just as Paul wrote to the church, as we consider others' interests to be more important than our own, we will be living more closely to the example set by Christ, Who is the true model of humility.

When I think of all the positive attributes, humility is the most important. If we are humble, it's impossible to be filled with pride. If we are humble, it is hard to be critical and unforgiving of others to a degree of bitterness.

John Baldoni, a leadership communications consultant who works with Fortune 500 companies and author of *Great Communication Secrets of Great Leaders*, says,

> Humility, however, is the grace note of leadership. One of the most humble leaders in the history of human expedition is Sir Ernest Shackleton. Although his voyage to Antarctica ended in disaster, he brought all of his men home safely. While he led from strength, he served with humility—he sought to make his team comfortable and assured throughout every phase of the long journey back to civilization. Humility is admission of humanity, a sense that leader and follower are in this together. That deepens a sense of trust. Better to admit a shortcoming or a limitation than to lead blindly onto the unknown.[17]

GRACE IS GIVEN TO THE HUMBLE

Proverbs 22:4 (NAS) says, "The reward of humility and the fear of the Lord are riches, honor and life." What more could we want?

St. Augustine says there are three virtues that are indispensable for being filled with the power of the Holy Spirit and necessary to enkindle the fire of His love. These three are humility, humility and humility! The Bible names only three people called "humble." They are Moses (Numbers 12:3), whom God chose to lead his people, the Virgin Mary (Luke 1:48–49), chosen for her humility to be the mother of God, and Jesus (Philippians 2:8–10), the Name that outshines all names.

Self-control is impossible without humility. Self-control is the ability to accept the reality that the only thing in life that you can change or control is yourself. Self-control is what keeps in check all other self-destructive behaviors such as addictions, obsessive/compulsive behavior and irrational rage. With self-control we are able to have a balance and focus that helps us cope with life's challenges. It helps keep us from overreacting and living in excess.

Without self-control, we easily fall prey to perfectionism, depression or the inability to maintain healthy emotional boundaries. We all know people who feel the need to manipulate, intimidate or fix everyone else in their life. This too is a self-control issue. They have lost sight of the boundary line that defines their life from ours. It is clear that self-ambition can ruin a friendship, a family and even a community like a church.

God is awesome and all the qualities we need to be our best are available simply by asking Him. Only He can give us the judgment, courage and stamina to accomplish this task of gaining humility and self-control. Changes become God's responsibility when we learn to ask humbly for God's help in our lives. We cannot accept credit, but we can give Him thanks and the glory.

Our commitment to face our character flaws and to admit them to others is a positive step forward. Sometimes God removes the destructive behavior pattern and sometimes He simply reinvents it. He may, for example, change a Bossy Bessie into a newborn leader. With the help of our Lord, all aspects of our lives can be rewarding.

As we continue to practice humility and accept God's teaching we will eventually begin to be more like Christ, sharing with others the blessings and love we have received.

SIMPLICITY MADE SIMPLE

As you trust in the Lord and show your willingness to become more Christlike, here are some inspirational steps to keep you on track:

TAKE A PERSONAL INVENTORY of your behavior traits. Which ones are destructive and which are positive? You cannot begin a journey to a more positive way of living unless you know what needs fixing. Review the following areas of your life and identify any areas in which you may need to apply self-control:

Personal: Eating habits, sugar intake, excessive shopping, cleaning, acceptance of self, love of others, body image and exercise.

Relational: Establishing emotional boundaries, handling anger or resentment, overidealism, use of intimidation and unconditional acceptance of love of others.

Work/School: Workaholic, assertiveness, self-recognition, fear of success, stress management, time management and perfectionism.

Community: Participation in church, clubs and other activities, leadership, competition, recreation and involvement with others.

CONFESS YOUR SINS TO GOD. All of us fall short of the glory of God. By practicing honest examination of ourselves weekly, combined with confession to God, we will in essence be practicing humility.

ACCEPT CORRECTION AND FEEDBACK GRACIOUSLY. This is hard, especially when the correction feels more like an attack. Our first response should be to simply thank the person for caring enough to share with us their concerns. Then we should pray that the Lord will show us what He is trying to teach us through this person.

HUMILITY means accepting a lower position than you expected with grace. Regardless of your seat at the table of life, you can still make a valuable contribution if you allow your pride to take a step back and recognize that your purpose may be to support others that are being lifted up.

CHOOSE TO SERVE. What greater example could we have than Christ Himself? When we serve others, we are serving God's purpose in our lives. As we change the focus from ourselves to others, we build the kingdom of God.

FORGIVE, FORGIVE AND KEEP ON FORGIVING. It is one of the greatest acts of humility.

GROW A GRATEFUL HEART. The more of an attitude of gratitude that you have, the more humility will fill your heart. Salvation alone is reason enough to be grateful!

KEEP PRIDE IN CHECK. Whenever pride sneaks its way into your heart, simply look toward the cross. It is impossible to be proud when you look at the very nature of God hanging on the cross. The Christian walk is a daily commitment of dying to self and living through Him.

Lord, I realize that every good thing in my life is from You. And every good quality that I may have is also a gift from You. Teach me practical ways to put the needs of others before my own so that I can grow in the character of Christ and serve You with a humble heart.

The Best Kind of Investment

And though I bestow all my goods to feed the poor,

and though I give my body to be burned,

and have not charity, it profiteth me nothing.

—1 CORINTHIANS 13:3 (KJV)

First Corinthians chapter 13 is often called the "love chapter" of the Bible. In these verses, Paul warned the believers in Corinth to be sure that their motive for service didn't lack real love or charity. Paul says here that love is more important than all the spiritual gifts. It is love and charity that make our actions and gifts useful. Real love involves unselfish service to others and shows you care about them. Love is the greatest of all human qualities and it is the attribute of God Himself. First John 4:16 declares that God *is* love.

God gave us spiritual gifts for life on earth in order to build each other up and to serve and strengthen our communities of both church and other. Faith is the foundation, and hope is the attitude and focus that brings righteous love into action. As 1 Corinthians 13:13 says, of faith, hope and charity, the greatest is charity. Only when faith and hope are in line, can we truly love with charity. As

Bruce Bickle and Stan Jantz wrote in *Simple Matters*, "There's only one motive that makes the service you deliver honorable and true, and that's love. And there's only one way for your service to come from a heart of love. God must be in it."[18]

As we make a commitment toward godly character, we realize that part of that commitment is to look beyond ourselves and love others the same way Christ did. He took on the role of servant, never exploiting His position of greatness or expecting to receive personal benefit from His service. When we look back on our lives, what do we hope to see? Should our epitaph read: "Lived the abundant life and acquired many possessions"? Or should it say: "In gratitude for her unfailing love and service to all."

When we realize that we may be the only expression of Christ that some may see, our responsibility to love others takes on a whole new level and meaning. As Kim Thomas wrote in her book *Simplicity*, "It is our purest form of worship to offer back our lives to God reflecting his image."[19] When we volunteer and provide charity to others, we are indeed offering God a reflection of His own demonstrated image of servanthood.

When I think about Christ's life, I realize that He was all about community. Christ volunteered His life to the *entire* community. His mission was among the people. How simple is that? He knew that the only way to change His world was by affecting it one person at a time. Christ's acceptance of and willingness to contribute to the lives of the individual would change the world. Unless we are willing to charitably give to others, we cannot affect the world with positive change.

Oscar Greene tells of an experience he had at church that changed his perspective and inspired him to volunteer. Oscar can't sing, and he says this embarrasses him.

At church, I retire to the back and just struggle along during hymns. But recently, an acquaintance said to me, "Of course you can sing. Why not 'sing' silently to God? I do this often, after retiring at night."

Only at night? I suddenly thought. *Why not during the day?* Then another thought burst into my mind: *Why not let my life do the singing?*

I began Sunday at church. When appointed ushers were absent, I volunteered to replace them without being asked. Following services, I removed bulletins from pew racks, tidied the hymnals and prayer books and pushed in the kneelers. Then I offered rides to those reluctant to ask or too fearful of imposing. In the days since then, I've discovered there are one hundred small ways I can "sing" silently to God through serving others . . . on Sunday and other days. (And I do sing songs of praise to God in my mind.)

Oscar then asks, "How can you 'sing' for God today?"[20]

VOLUNTEERING HAS GREAT RETURNS

What I find amazing is that when we give real charity to others, we benefit too. When we experience the joy of connecting with others it makes us whole. It heals us, challenges us and teaches us the true meaning of real love. The most memorable moments of our lives usually involve people that we have cared for. And there are even further benefits to helping others. Community Service Volunteers (CSV), a volunteer services organization in the United Kingdom, announced research reporting that volunteering fights obesity and improves health and fitness. Of a survey of more than six hundred volunteers nearly forty-seven percent said their health and fitness improved since volunteering. Of the eighteen- to twenty-four-year-olds that volunteered, nearly thirty-two percent said it helped them lose weight and cut down on alcohol.

That said, the true benefit of showing love to others is received when your motive for charity is righteous. As Paul taught, the best gifts for the wrong reason have no profit. Examine your heart, if your reason for service involves guilt, personal satisfaction, pride or hopeful reward, then your motive is not one of love.

As we read earlier, Philippians 2:3–4 warns us to do nothing out of selfish ambition or vain conceit but in humility consider others better than ourselves. Each of us should look not only to our own interests but also to the interests of others.

Accountability, appreciation of God, giving glory to God, and obedience are all good reasons for volunteering your time as charity to others. Ultimately, it is our love for God that should motivate us to charity. If our focus is on God, then we will be more interested in others than ourselves. Consequently, we will be patient and kind and not boastful or proud. We cannot be rude or self-seeking if we are seeking after and honoring our Lord.

Remember, "You, my brothers, were called to be free. But do not use your freedom to indulge the sinful nature; rather, serve one another in love. The entire law is summed up in a single command: 'Love your neighbor as yourself'" (Galatians 5:13–14, NIV).

If we invest in others, we are imitating Christ—and that is a very good way to live.

SIMPLICITY MADE SIMPLE

Here are some thoughts to consider as you look for ways to invest your spiritual gifts in the community of service:

As with any good work, having a plan for **FINDING THE RIGHT VOLUNTEER WORK** is important. First, examine yourself. What do you want to do? What do you enjoy doing? How are you prepared to give? By assessing your talents, values, interests and abilities, you can make a better decision toward charity.

GIVE financially if you cannot give of your time. If you cannot give financially, then pray for a ministry and its staff and volunteers.

Most **VOLUNTEER WORK INVOLVES A TEAM EFFORT**. Team effort requires flexibility, adaptability and a positive attitude toward others. Good communication skills and being comfortable in social situations are positive qualities that best translate to a team effort.

HERE ARE SOME IDEAS to consider as possible areas to place your time or money for charity. For the volunteer who cannot or prefers not to volunteer on-site, The Virtual Volunteering Project (www.serviceleader.org/new/virtual) is a possibility. Launched in 1996, the project makes it possible for people who cannot volunteer on-site to volunteer through the Internet. The American Hospital Association (AHA) sponsors the American Society of Directors of Volunteer Services, which publishes a journal and holds an annual conference. The American Association of Retired Persons (AARP) Web site (www.aarp.org) hosts a series of well-designed pages related to the importance of volunteering, including a guide to volunteering and links to a variety of organizations offering opportunities to volunteer. The Corporation for National and Community Service officially represents three important national service initiatives: AmenCorps (the domestic Peace Corps), Learn and Serve America and the National Senior Service Corps. The corporation's Web site (www.cns.gov) allows searches at the community level for volunteer opportunities and is a good starting point when looking for a volunteer or national service experience.

There are many different ways that you can **HELP OTHERS IN YOUR COMMUNITY**. You can help others complete their tax returns, learn defensive driving techniques, get a job and apply for public benefits for which they qualify. In doing so, you help others maintain their dignity, independence and sense of purpose.

BE A TROOP LEADER. Today, millions of adults provide leadership and mentoring to Brownies and Cub Scout packs, Girl Scout and Boy Scout troops, and Venturing crews. Together, these volunteers gave millions of hours of service in years past to ensure that the youth of America have access to and benefit from Scouting programs in their communities. Through the work of these many volunteers, the Girl Scouts and Boy Scouts remain the foremost youth programs of character development and values-based leadership training in America. Research reveals that people with strong Scouting experience often demonstrate higher ethical and moral standards than non-Scouts.

Father, I want to offer my time and services to help others in Your name. Show me ways that I can demonstrate Your love and influence in the community in which I live. May my life reflect the kindness You have shown me through kind acts I can do for others.

PART FOUR

God Has a Health Plan for You

THE WAY TO MAINTAIN overall health is to develop a spiritual relationship with God. A quiet time sitting in a garden or walking in a park to focus on His presence can empower us with the insight that we need to live a balanced life. He may tell us to do less in one area and focus more time on another, guaranteeing success if we learn to obey His voice within us. Remember, God is with us even when we can't *feel* His presence. But if we develop the habit of looking for Him, we will see Him in everything that is taking place around us. There is more to life than what we see now—God has a heavenly plan for those who abide in Him.

A Thirsty Heart

We are troubled on every side, yet not distressed;

we are perplexed, but not in despair.

—2 CORINTHIANS 4:8 (KJV)

I love this verse because all of us can relate to a time when we were at the end of our ropes and about to despair. Paul reminds us that even then, we are never at the end of hope. Although we live in perishable bodies that suffer and sin, God never abandons us.

One of the most powerful books I have read is *The Sacred Romance* by Brent Curtis and John Eldredge. This book describes the difference between living a life *in* relationship with God and one *without*. Living outside of relationship is like living with a lost heart. Here is how the authors describe it: "For what shall we do when we wake one day to find we have lost touch with our heart and with it the very refuge where God's presence resides?"[21]

Most of us have gone through times when we lived only outside our heart. We focused on our life at work, play, church and family. Those are the times when we felt out of touch with our *heart*selves because we were out of touch with God. Our prayer life seemed dry and we struggled to even feel the presence of God. We went to church hoping to be moved by the service only to be, once again, let down and disappointed. We were like empty shells whose outer lives show success and wear the happy "life-is-great" face for the entire world to see. But inside, we have lost our passion and our dreams. This is when our fears surface. This is when our deepest wounds hurt the most. And unlike our outer selves, we cannot pacify the heart with more money, more success or another title after our names. The heart is thirsty. The great Christian commentator A. W. Tozer says, "As the hart panteth after the water brooks, so panteth my soul after thee, O God. My soul thirsteth for God, for the living God: when shall I come and appear before God?" Thirsty hearts are those whose longings have been wakened by the touch of God within them.

There is nothing sadder than someone who chooses to ignore the wakening touch of God on his or her heart. My ex-husband was blessed with success in business, sports, education and intelligence. Midway through his life, God touched his heart. This was the toughest challenge he had ever faced. He turned to an old college friend but couldn't find a solution to his struggle. Then he turned to me. As we sat talking, tears began to form in his eyes as he told me about the hole he had discovered in his heart. He said he didn't know how to fill it and he wanted me to tell him what the Bible had to say about such a thing.

As we talked through that evening, I prayed and I hoped that he would accept the invitation that God had given him. But he didn't. Soon the downward spiral began. It was like a whirlwind and all of his life was caught in it: his business, his self-esteem, his thirsty heart and me.

It is when God touches our hearts that we first realize there is a spiritual dimension to the external world. If we listen and accept His call on our hearts, our lives will be filled with a new awareness that comes only from the Spirit of God. It can be described as living with intimacy. Life is fuller and laughter is sweeter when we live entirely aware of God's presence because we are responding to the most powerful part of our being. A relationship with our Creator makes us whole.

Our great God Who rules the world cares about each of us. We were created to commune with Him. Although sin marred the perfect original relationship Adam and Eve had with God, God still wants us to want Him. He calls us to Himself; all we have to do is respond. As the old hymn says, God wants us to "come to the garden alone, while the dew is still on the roses" and to "walk with Him and talk with Him." To have a healthy spirit is as simple as a walk in the (park) garden. So why do we find it so hard to remember this when our lives seem to be without light? Robert Benson, author of *Living Prayer*, says, "The liturgical calendar can open our hearts and minds and ears to our own story if we will listen. It will teach us that there will be times for us when our prayer will be that of those who live in darkness and times when it will be that of those who live in light."[22] The calendar is a reminder that light always follows dark, just as the Resurrection followed Christ's death and Sunday followed Good Friday.

RETURN TO YOUR FIRST LOVE DAILY

We all yearn to live as if life were a new romance. The innocent giddiness of new love is intoxicating. We wait with bated breath for every word our new love has to say. We spend every available moment in his or her presence.

God invites you to return to your "first" love every day. But as with any meaningful relationship, it takes two. Love is a two-way street. Imagine a relationship, with only one participant. Imagine how you would feel to always be the pursuer—an unrequited love, if you will. Most of us would lose our resolve and give up on a relationship like that, but not God. He says, "If anyone is thirsty, let him come to me and drink. Whoever believes in me . . . streams of living water will flow from within him" (John 7:37–38, NIV). The love affair of our lives is the one we have in our heart. God tells us in Proverbs 4:23 (NIV) to "Above all else, guard your heart, for it is the wellspring of life." If we lose our hearts, we lose everything.

Like good wine, love is meant to get better with time. As we learn to hear the voice of our First Love, we open our lives to a new romance that only our *heart* can hear.

SIMPLICITY MADE SIMPLE

Here are some thoughts to help as you journey to a deeper renewed relationship with the love of your heart and your soul:

My friend Lynn Morrissey suggests **WRITING A LOVE LETTER TO GOD**. As Lynn expresses it, "Though my journal is yet empty, I know it has hardly room to contain the love I want to express to God because of His measureless love for me—hardly enough room to contain the gratitude I owe Him for transforming my life through His gift of written prayer."[23]

LISTEN TO THE RHYTHM OF YOUR HEART. As God calls to us, we must learn to get in sync with His rhythm, which is often different from the rhythm we have set for our lives. Make a list of all the activities that now fill your life. Then look for ways to incorporate more time with the Love of your heart. If possible, write appointments in your calendar for daily, weekly and monthly dates with the Lord.

EXAMINE YOUR LIFE TODAY. Is it one of light or darkness? As novelist Sue Monk Kidd wrote, "If God seems distant, guess who moved?" Our hearts migrate. We must recognize that our busy, cluttered lives leave no time to be near God. God hasn't moved, we have. Look at your own spiritual migration and determine where you heart is located. Are you coming or going?

What is God's purpose for your life? Only when we are clear about our **PURPOSE** will we be able to walk in rhythm with God. To make your journey purposeful, try writing a biblically driven mission statement for your life. *The Purpose-Driven Life* by Rick Warren is a must-read for all who are searching for purpose and meaning in their life.

Read the love letter God has sent to you through His written Word. We cannot love someone we do not know. Unless we spend time **READING THE SCRIPTURES**, reading the letter written for our hearts, we will starve from spiritual malnutrition.

PRAY. This is the one Love that will never get tired of hearing you talk! The dialog is never finished. This relationship includes a never-ending dialog. Explore various prayer traditions from contemplative prayer and meditation to intercessory and written prayer. Keep a prayer journal. You will be amazed at the response you will receive from the Love of your heart.

Lord, I know that You love me with an everlasting love, and though I cannot comprehend how great a love You have for me, my greatest joy comes when I am aware of Your presence. Today, I will keep my ears bent for Your voice and listen for Your sweet guidance through whatever I may have to face.

The Most Important Conversation

And pray in the Spirit on all occasions with all kinds
of prayers and requests. With this in mind, be alert
and always keep on praying for all the saints.

—EPHESIANS 6:18 (NIV)

My goddaughter was going through her normal teenage rebellious stage. As we sat down for dinner, I asked her to lead the prayer. Her response was, "Why should I pray?" My first reaction was one of shock and indignation that she would ask such a question. But after thinking about it, I realized that it was a reasonable question from a thinking person. As a child, she simply accepted prayer as a fact of life. Now, as she approached adulthood, she was processing and questioning the things she had accepted unexamined before. Unless she could indeed have good reason for doing things, I came to see, she wouldn't and shouldn't continue with them.

Now I was asking the question: Why should we pray? Of course, the easy answer is because the Bible instructs us to do so. But there obviously had to be more to it than that. As I wrote earlier, God wants a relationship with us. Prayer is our dialog with Him. It is a way for us to get to know Him. Unless we get to know Him, we will never know the plans He has for us. Jeremiah 29:11 tells us that God has special plans for our lives, plans to bless us and make us prosper. This is wonderful, but the next two verses spell out the conditions necessary to receive the benefit of His plans, "Then you will call upon Me and go and pray to Me, and I will listen to you. And you will seek Me and find Me, when you search for Me with all your heart" (Jeremiah 29:12–13, NKJV). As we learn to know God's will for our lives, we are able to bend our wills so that they align with His.

Guideposts writer Eleanor Sass wrote about a time she was struggling to get her physical will in line with God's will for her spiritual life. If you own a pet, then you know that they have a built-in clock that is set to go off at meal times. Eleanor's dachshund, Heidi, had such a clock. Heidi's internal alarm went off twice a day—morning and evening. Here's her story:

> I never thought that Heidi's alarm would help me, but it has. I was having a difficult time disciplining myself to wake up half an hour earlier in the morning in order to have a quiet time. No matter how I planned or how many resolutions I made, when morning came and my alarm clock sounded I'd hit the button, and roll over for another half hour of shut-eye. Finally, I knew I had to ask God for help. So one night before retiring, I told Him I was trusting Him to get me up the next day.
>
> In the morning, before my alarm clock went off, Heidi did

something she had never done before. She leapt onto my bed, padded up to my pillow and began licking my closed eyelids with her wet tongue. I groaned. Through one eye I glanced at the clock. I'd forgotten about my conversation with God the night before.

Go away Heidi, I pleaded. It's not breakfast time yet. Then I tried to go back to sleep, but Heidi wouldn't let me. She bounced around on the bed and continued smothering my face with her wet kisses. Now I was wide awake. So I got up and fed her. Then I had my quiet time.

Heidi has kept to this morning ritual ever since. Who says God doesn't have a sense of humor . . . or that He doesn't answer prayers?[24]

As Eleanor attempted to align her will with God's, He gave her the ability to accomplish it with a little help from Heidi.

God is also the source of abundant power, and unless we go to Him and ask for it, we will never receive this amazing gift. Through Him we gain knowledge that enables us to grow and mature in our Christian walk. Just as our earthly gardens need sun in order to grow to maturity and ripen for the purpose of providing nutritious food, so too is God the sunshine for our spiritual lives. Without His abundant power we will remain as unripened fruit.

Ephesians 6:18 instructs us to pray with all kinds of prayers. This indicates that there must be more than one kind of prayer, and there is; various prayers include meditation, confession, adoration, submission and petition. The sad thing is that for most of us, petition is the most familiar.

Let's just focus on meditation for the moment. Christians are clearly instructed to meditate on the Scriptures. Psalm 119:148 (NKJV) says, "My eyes are awake through the night watches that I may meditate on Your word." Romans 10:17 (KJV) teaches that faith comes from *hearing* the word, and we all could certainly use more faith. That word is meant to go to our hearts. The psalmist says, "I desire to do your will, O my God; your law is within my heart" (Psalm 40:8, NIV). From these descriptions it is clear that meditation on the Bible is part of prayer.

PONDER THE WORD OF GOD

One of the easiest ways to meditate and hear the Word is simply to pray the Scriptures. I especially like to pray God's promises. When I hear His promises reverberating into my head from my mouth, it assures me on a deeper level than simply reading them would do. Perhaps it is because I am a verbal person, which is a nice way of saying that I talk all the time! At least when I am praying the Scriptures, I can be assured that my words are more than mere chatter. I believe all of us have experienced times when our prayer life seemed as dry as a desert. Unconfessed sin can rob us of our ability to pray with faith. When we are in sin, we are out of relationship with God. How can we go to Him with petitions unless we first confess our sins? Often, it is during meditation that I become aware of unconfessed sins. Perhaps this is one reason we are instructed to meditate. Unless we know God's will, we cannot know if we are in it or out of it in sin. Sometimes, we have a dark spot on our hearts from long ago. We can feel the darkness, but we can't identify what is causing it. Then, in the midst of prayer, God reminds us of a long-forgotten sin. This is His loving reminder that He wants to have a closer relationship with us.

His reminder is our opportunity to confess even the oldest of sins. By humbling ourselves at His feet and asking for forgiveness, we are easily made aware of how awesome God truly is. Psalm 68:20 declares that God is a God Who saves us. How can we not feel adoration toward a God Who so willingly forgives humble creatures like us?

I have always been "wowed" at the amazing beauty of a sunset. If I could paint, I would paint the sky at sunset. For me, this is God's artistry. I cannot even imagine how beautiful God Himself must be. Psalm 19:1 (NIV) says, "The heavens declare the glory of God; the skies proclaim the work of his hands." As I sit in wonder over the work of His hands, I am led to submission. I pray that as I grow in my prayer life, I will be able to completely submit my life and my body as worship to my Creator.

As you learn to pray the various prayers, remember to guard your heart from temptation and to pray for wisdom. When I wake in the middle of the night, I ask God to tell me who to pray for—after all, if I am going to be up in the middle of the night, I might as well be useful.

SIMPLICITY MADE SIMPLE

Here are some thoughts to help you find your unique prayer walk:

The easiest way to make prayer a regular part of your day is to match your prayer time and style with your personality and life. If you are a night owl, then set aside time for prayer before going to bed. I am a morning person, which makes early morning the ideal quiet time for me. Then **SET UP A PRAYER "CLOSET."** A prayer closet is simply a place where you can easily go to find quiet time with God.

Make and **KEEP A LIST** of those you want to remember in prayer. Then add to it as God brings people to mind. As your prayers are answered you can note and date the answers alongside your list.

BEGIN YOUR PRAYERS WITH THANKSGIVING. The Word says, "Enter his gates with thanksgiving and his courts with praise" (Psalm 100:4, NIV). We have so many things to thank God for. Start by thanking Him for His patience and forgiveness, and the very privilege of being able to come into His presence for prayer. Then thank Him for all the things He has done in your life recently.

INTERCESSORY PRAYER is the most powerful way to affect others. There are always people for whom we can pray. Simply begin by praying for your friends and neighbors. Then pray for our country, our leaders and for your church. Of course, pray for any special request or those that God brings to mind.

One of the most compelling books I have read on prayer is Stormie Omartian's *The Power of a Praying Wife*. She also has a book for husbands. Her prayers are powerful yet simple. For me, her book has made praying for my husband **MORE PERSONAL AND SPECIAL.**

PRAY TOGETHER. Our small group prays in a circle. Before we pray everyone gives a prayer request. Then as we move around the circle each one of us prays for one of the prayer requests. It is a simple yet powerful way to pray. Hearing your friends pray out loud for your need is profoundly faith filling. God promises that when two or three or more are gathered, He too is there (see Matthew 18:20). I know without a doubt that the presence of God is in that circle of prayer.

Lord, "I will meditate on all your works and consider all your mighty deeds. Your ways, O God, are holy. What god is so great as our God? You are the God who performs miracles; you display your power among the peoples" (Psalm 77:12–14, NIV). I put my trust in You alone.

God Is Great!

If we confess our sins, he is faithful and just and will
forgive us our sins and purify us from all unrighteousness.

—1 JOHN 1:9 (NIV)

I cannot even imagine what being pure is. Yet this verse is God's promise to us that if we confess our sins, He will *purify* us from *all* unrighteousness. Whew . . . I cannot fathom such an event. I was raised during the 1950s and '60s. It was an interesting time for America. I like to think that, somehow, my generation helped to contribute to the "enlightenment" of the times. I know I was full of questions. "Why?" seemed to be my response to almost everything that the church said I should do. And the answer I received most frequently was, because it's a "mystery." Of course, this only prompted me to ask more questions. Ultimately, my questions led me on a ten-year search of and for religion. In the end, what I found was simple faith in the love of Jesus.

Yet all these years later, I am still awed at the prospect of such an amazing gift as forgiveness, which was a central message in Jesus' teachings. We don't have to jump through hoops. We don't have to earn our way. We don't have to put on shrouds and drag ourselves through the streets. We don't have to be flogged—though we still must face the consequences of our actions. But that is exactly what many of us do when we feel guilty. The pain of guilt has two sides. It can be the guilt we feel over something we have done wrong. Or it can be the pain we feel that is caused by a misdeed or a wrong against us; we can even feel guilty for bringing the offense upon ourselves.

In either case, it's painful. Sometimes that pain can fester for years as a grudge held against another. What I find interesting about this application of guilt is that we can end up hurting ourselves even more. With our "I'll never forgive (or forget)" attitude, we demonstrate our own lack of love. Then we use that "terrible" offense as a reason for everything that either has gone wrong or is wrong with our lives.

Our own inability to forgive ourselves is even more insidious. It destroys our self-esteem and causes anxiety that goes to our core—our soul—leaving us feeling so unworthy that we reject the very love that God has offered us. But Romans 3:23 says all have sinned and fallen short of the glory of God.

No matter who you are, you are not alone when it comes to sin. We are all guilty. That is exactly the reason God sent His Son to redeem us. In His gracious love, He knew we could not live a perfect life. And what a blessing we have in His forgiving love. As author W. Phillip Keller wrote, "Pure joy! Such is the liberation of a spirit set free from the tormenting tensions of guilt, self-accusation, and feeling unforgiven. Only the man or woman who knows such release is in turn able to extend complete and wholehearted forgiveness to fellow human beings."[25]

GUILT CAN BE QUICKLY FORGIVEN

God is so great that only He can bring good things out of bad. We must learn that we can truly be honest with God about how we have messed up, or about how angry we are over something. God can take the truth. God wants the truth. God forgives the sin and moves on. He doesn't dwell on our mistakes and shortcomings. Even when we mess up horribly, He still has a wonderful way of bringing beauty out of bad circumstances or consequences. He is gentle and kind and wishes that none of us should perish. His love is that big. His love is unconditional. His love is delightfully free. His love changes us. Once we experience the forgiving freedom of His love, it will be impossible for us to harbor a grievance against another.

God's love also makes us more aware. Guideposts writer Phyllis Hobe wrote about an experience she had regarding awareness of sin.

> One day when I was at the supermarket checkout, the cashier, who was very young, pointed to a bag of fresh cranberries and asked me what they were. I couldn't believe she didn't know.
>
> "They're cranberries," I said, with one of those "Gee, how dumb can you be?" laughs. I regretted it almost immediately, and even more so when I saw the hurt in the girl's eyes.
>
> "I never saw them before," she explained. "I've only seen them come out of cans." Of course, I realized; she had grown up in a time when almost every kind of food was processed. "But you didn't have to laugh at me," she added gently.
>
> The first thing that came to my mind was an excuse: I hadn't meant to hurt you; I had spoken without thinking. Then I realized that I wasn't being honest with myself. What I meant

didn't matter. The fact was that I had hurt someone, and that was wrong.

As the girl handed my change and receipt, I held onto her hand. "Please, can you forgive me?" I asked her.

"It's okay," she said, shaking her head. "It's not important."

"Yes, it is," I said. "You're important, and I'm sorry I hurt you. I need your forgiveness." I prayed she would understand how much I meant it.

She did. With a little smile, she squeezed my hand and said, "You're forgiven."

When we think about sins, we tend to think in big terms. But it's the little sins that are likely to slip by unnoticed, and they can hurt people too. Making excuses doesn't change what we did, but asking forgiveness can change us—for the better.[26]

Luke 6:31 (NIV) says to "do to others as you would have them do to you." Phyllis did exactly that. But I doubt she would have given this incident much thought if she hadn't already experienced forgiveness in her own life.

Our willingness to be humble gives us a new perspective that places us in agreement with God.

SIMPLICITY MADE SIMPLE

Here are some thoughts that may help you find a new perspective and the joy of living a life of forgiveness:

Forgiveness is not automatic. The Bible gives us clear direction. As 1 John 1:9 says, we must *confess* our sins. We must recognize where we have erred and hurt God by our actions. When **CONFESSING OUR SINS** to God, we must be as specific as possible. General confessions bring little to conviction, or do little to convince God that we are serious.

The next step in receiving forgiveness is to **TURN AWAY FROM DOING WRONG**. If we are serious about changing our ways, and overcoming sin, God will give us the grace to do it. If we just give God lip service, with no intention of changing, it is as if we are mocking God. It is only when we come to Him with humility and sincerity that His abundant grace can be made available. True repentance gives us the power of the Holy Spirit to make the needed changes in our lives.

True **REPENTANCE AND HUMILITY** are always accompanied by the action of asking forgiveness of all those we have wronged and to make restitution to them. Matthew 5:23–24 says to first be reconciled and then come and offer your gifts of restitution.

FORGIVE OTHERS. Mark 11:25–26 (AMP) says if you have anything against anyone, forgive him and let it drop, leave it, let it go, in order that your Father Who is in heaven may also forgive you. If we receive God's forgiveness, it is our duty to forgive those who have wronged us. God will not forgive us unless we forgive others—plain and simple. Sometimes we carry bitterness so long that it becomes part of our nature clouding our souls and causing a constant anxiety in our being. No matter how deep your hurt is, God wants to release you from it. He loves you and wants to heal you. It is because of His great love for you that He is calling you to forgive. It is only then that you can be released from your pain.

No sin is too great for **GOD'S LOVING FORGIVENESS**. Jesus said in John 6:37 (AMP), "All whom My Father gives (entrusts) to Me will come to Me; and the one who comes to Me I will most certainly not cast out [I will never, no never, reject one of them who comes to Me]." His promises are true. Even if you do not feel forgiven, but have confessed your sin with sincerity, you are forgiven by God. Do not believe otherwise. If God has forgiven you—who are you to question His authority?

TAKE TIME FOR REFLECTION. With thoughtful reflection ask God to help you recall mistakes you have made. Then agree to take responsibility for the harm you have done and ask forgiveness.

Father in heaven, I know I am guilty of sinning
against You, and I know I have hurt other people, just as
I have been hurt by them. Please forgive me for my
trespasses, as I forgive those who trespass against me.
Lead me to the freedom from guilt so that I can enjoy
the abundant life Jesus came to give to me.

We Are Never Alone

Let your conduct be without covetousness; be content
with such things as you have. For He Himself has said,
"I will never leave you nor forsake you."

—HEBREWS 13:5 (NKJV)

Most of us have experienced the heartache of feeling abandoned or betrayed by someone we thought really cared for us. Too many marriages dissolve in divorce. When relationships break apart, the vows of "forever" crumble along with our hearts.

God promises to *never* leave us. But after all of life's disappointments, we can find it hard to believe even His promise to us. Yet, as Christians, trusting God is a foundation of our faith. Numbers 23:19 (NIV) says, "God is not a man, that he should lie, nor a son of man, that he should change his mind."

Why is it, then, that when troubled or in need of advice, we find it easier to turn to the professionals in the world and our friends but forget to include our Maker? John 15 says that if we abide in Him, He will abide in us. God wants to live with us. He wants to walk with us and talk with us. He wants to be our Counselor, our Friend and our Lover.

Why is it when we feel discontent or restless we look to replace those feelings with worldly things? We seek more toys, or pursue more activities. It seems the more we seek, the more restless we get. God promises to give us the desires of our heart. Yet we fail to realize that the greatest desire of our heart is a meaningful relationship with Him. And nothing else can take His place.

I am amazed when I read in the Psalms about David—a man who probably had one of the closest friendships with God—struggling to feel near to Him. In Psalm 13:1, David cries out to the Lord, asking Him why He is hiding from him. David felt alone; he could not feel the presence of God. That is what happens to us, which may be the answer as to why we forget to turn to God when we need help. Our mere mortal selves think that unless we *feel* the presence of God, He is not there. But that is not true. That is cynicism robbing us of the truth about God's ever-abiding love and omnipresence in our lives. God has promised to *never* leave us. But He has not promised that we will always be able to *feel* Him.

In fact, sometimes it seems as though God purposely hides His presence from us, which is why we may feel estranged or even abandoned by Him. We pray. And we wait to hear from God. But He seems silent. Our prayer life gets as dry as the desert. Soon, we feel as if we have spent forty days, or forty years, aimlessly walking and waiting. As hard and lonely as these times can feel, they are necessary for every Christian in order to develop a deeper faith. The Word says, "Now faith is being sure of what we hope for and certain of what we do not see" (Hebrews 11:1, NIV). Faith isn't necessary when answers are clear to us. Our faith is strengthened only when we *trust* that God is keeping His promise; faith grows as we become certain of what we cannot see.

IF YOU SEEK GOD YOU WILL FIND HIM

Remember the adage, "Absence makes the heart grow fonder"? This is the perfect application for it. When we are feeling as if God is hiding from us, we must consider how we would respond if God were our earthly love. When our loves are away, we miss them but we don't feel abandoned. Instead, with each passing day, we anticipate their return. Our passion and our love grow more intense. This is exactly how God wants us to respond when we feel far away from Him.

Unfortunately, too often we put more credence in our *feelings* than our faith. I remember when I first realized that worship wasn't about my feeling good. How could I have been so confused? Of course worship had nothing to do with how I felt. Instead, it has everything to do with God. The whole point was for me to humble myself at His feet and praise Him whether I felt a special tingly feeling or not.

When I hear someone say, "I didn't get anything out of that service. I just didn't feel the presence of God," I wonder, *How did we get so confused?* It's not just feelings that matter. What matters is that we focus on Who God is and on His unchanging nature. Regardless of our circumstances or how we feel, God is unchanging. He keeps His promises to us. He will never leave us. He is always with us. Whether we are in the grocery store, at home, work or in the midst of an argument with our mates: He is with us.

Guideposts writer Barbara Chafin wrote about being surprised by God's presence in the ordinary moments of life:

> Recently I felt a special closeness to God in the nursing home, sitting for hours beside my unresponsive mother who had Alzheimer's disease and had suffered a stroke. After her

death, I felt His comfort through the many friends and family members who extended their love and sympathy to me.

I've sensed God's Presence in more ordinary times, in the garden as I delight in the first green shoots of my vegetables breaking through the earth; or when I'm doing housework, polishing the antique chest that has been in our family for generations. I'm grateful that God doesn't limit Himself to meeting me in church.

Looking back over my life has given me the desire to look for God at all times in my life, so that I won't be like Jacob who didn't know God was "in this place." I do know that God is with me in every place. Even now.[27]

God loves you. No matter how you *feel*, God loves you so much that He sent His only Son to die for you. He yearns to shower you with attention. He is excited to tell you about the plans He has for your life. He is the lover of your soul. He is always waiting for you.

SIMPLICITY MADE SIMPLE

Here are some things to think about as you keep your sights on your First Love, the true Source of simplicity:

We must individually **BE COMMITTED TO JESUS CHRIST**; then we can know and experience God's love and plan for our lives. The Bible says, "Yet to all who received him, to those who believed in his name, he gave the right to become

GOD HAS A HEALTH PLAN FOR YOU

children of God" (John 1:12, NIV). Accepting Jesus means believing that Jesus is the Son of God, Who He claimed to be, then inviting Him to guide and direct our lives and make us into new people (see John 3:1–8).

God wants His people to have more than an intellectual understanding of the principles of His kingdom—more than a mere awareness of His existence. His desire for us is that we might enter into a **VERY PERSONAL AND INTIMATE RELATIONSHIP WITH HIM**. This relationship is not based on "head knowledge" (see Jeremiah 9:23–24), but on "heart knowledge" (see Jeremiah 31:33–34).

Remember that God's omnipresence is different than the manifestation of His presence. **GOD IS ALWAYS PRESENT** even when we are not aware of Him. He is always with us. And He is everywhere. His presence is too profound to be measured by our mortal emotions.

As with all meaningful relationships, **TRUE INTIMACY TAKES TIME**. Unless we spend time with our Soul Lover, we will not experience the intimate relationship He offers to us. God pursues us and He wants us to pursue Him.

GOD SPEAKS TO US. Sometimes He speaks through the Holy Spirit. Other times He speaks through the Bible, prayer or even our circumstances. If we listen, He will reveal Himself and His plans for us.

TRUST GOD. It is at life's worst moments that we have the greatest opportunity for the most intimate relationship with God. When we have nowhere else to turn, we can turn to Him. Sometimes when life is going well, I miss the intimacy that I experienced during those difficult times. Of course, God hasn't changed, I have. He is still right here at my elbow, watching, listening and ready to offer guidance at a moment's notice.

Lord, "Truly you are a God who hides himself" (Isaiah 45:15, NIV), but I understand that You do this so that I will seek You. You have promised that I will find You when I seek for You with my whole heart. So today I will look everywhere for You; and I know I will find You in the midst of everything that happens to me today.

Heaven

And I saw a new heaven and a new earth:

for the first heaven and the first earth were

passed away; and there was no more sea.

—REVELATION 21:1 (KJV)

The other day I was talking with a friend about praying. His daughter is five years old and he prays with her every night at bedtime. Recently, she has become inquisitive as to what is going on in heaven. She wants to know if God is reading bedtime stories to His children. And she wants to know what the children are learning. Her questions continue every evening. My friend is beginning to feel a bit inadequate because he isn't sure how to answer all her questions.

How would you describe heaven? Most of us, just like my friend's daughter, created an image of heaven in our minds when we were children. Children think about heaven a lot. But how much thought have you given to heaven recently? Try thinking about heaven now, as an adult. What does it look like? What does it feel like? Why would you want to go there? Too many of us struggle with life here on earth because we expect the Christian life to be a bit like heaven. We want "heaven" on earth, and being in touch with the spirit of simple living can perhaps give us glimpses of it. The problem is that we can't ultimately have heaven on earth. The verse on the previous page tells us that this earth will pass away. Even the current heaven is going to pass away. God is preparing a new home for us.

In Revelation 21, John is given a vision of the new heaven. As you read through his description it is clear that words cannot describe the beauty of it. The sight is so incredible that it is beyond description. John uses the most precious jewels to describe it as an attempt to give us a glimpse of what he saw. He uses jasper, a clear gem like a diamond, to describe the huge stone he saw on the throne. John tells of lightning and thundering, which is a reminder that God is about to judge Earth for the rejection of His Son Jesus Christ. And finally, John describes the sea of glass that is associated with the throne of God in heaven throughout the Bible (see Exodus 24:10).

John goes on to say,

> I saw the Holy City, the new Jerusalem, coming down out of heaven from God, prepared as a bride beautifully dressed for her husband.
>
> And I heard a loud voice from the throne saying, "Now the dwelling of God is with men, and he will live with them. They will be his people, and God himself will be with them and be their God.
>
> He will wipe every tear from their eyes. There will be no more death or mourning or crying or pain, for the old order of things has passed away."
>
> (Revelation 21:2–4, NIV)

Ponder for a moment what it will be like to live in a place of laughter without tears, life without death, and pleasure without pain!

Then beginning in verse 15, John continues with a stunning description of the new Jerusalem and even gives us measurements as to the size of this new heavenly city. They are given in cubits, which are multiples of twelve. This is symbolic because there were twelve tribes of Israel and twelve apostles. This new city is a perfect cube, twelve thousand furlongs wide and twelve thousand furlongs high. A furlong is equal to approximately 1,400–1,500 miles. This means that the first floor of the new Jerusalem will be fifteen thousand times as big as London. Or ten times as big as Germany. Let me repeat—that's just the first floor!

This will be a Holy City, with no sin, no lies and no evil. I cannot even imagine. There will be a river of life and a tree of life that will provide twelve different fruits each month for us to eat. Remember the tree in the Garden of Eden? This one is even better.

As amazing as all of these descriptions sound, they are not the most amazing or the most important description of the new heaven. The most important part is the fact that this is where God resides, and one day He will visibly live with us.

In Revelation 4:2–6, John says that as he looked upon the One sitting on the throne, it was like looking at jasper and a sardine stone and there was a rainbow around the throne. In order to truly appreciate the beauty of heaven, we must not forget the description of hell. Hell is a place of eternal pain and torment. It is fire, brimstone and darkness (see Revelation 21:8). It is total separation from God and all the comfort His presence brings.

THE BEST IS YET TO COME

The new Jerusalem is where God will dwell among us, His people who put their hope in Him and trust Jesus as their Savior. God will wipe away all our tears. There will be no more death. And we will be completely fulfilled with eternal joy. It will be more wonderful than we can ever imagine. *We will finally be home.*

It can be hard to even think about such joy when life's trials are beating us down. Guideposts writer Carol Kuykendall relays an interesting experience she had about earth, trials and heaven.

> Last week, something happened that changed my perspective. Our dear minister Dr. Bob died of a rare lung disease at the age of seventy. At his memorial service a family member passed on his final message to us, the flock he shepherded for twenty-five years. "Tell them," he whispered near death with a faint smile, "the best is yet to come!"
>
> I now repeat that hopeful promise to myself whenever I start worrying about aging—or any other problems, for that matter. And even when I get forgetful, I vow not to forget those comforting words.[28]

Our promise is in heaven. Our promise is to finally *know* the one true God. When life's hardships, struggles and disasters seem too much to bear, remember that we have a sure escape to a paradise of perfect peace, comfort and health.

SIMPLICITY MADE SIMPLE

Psychologist Larry Crabb has a terrific way of describing God's desire for an intimate, living relationship with us in his book *Shattered Dreams* when he says,

GOD HAS A HEALTH PLAN FOR YOU

We will encounter Christ as our best friend when shattered dreams help us become aware of

    . . . the strength of our desire to know Him

    . . . how unworthy we are to receive even the smallest expression of kindness from Him

    . . . the intensity of His longing to draw us into satisfying, soul-thrilling intimacy with Him and His Father (which, in His mind, is the greatest blessing He can give and worth whatever it takes for Him to give it and for us to receive it)

    . . . the unparalled value of intimacy with Him.[29]

The way to heaven is clear. In John 14:6 (KJV), Jesus said, "I am the way, the truth, and the life: no man cometh unto the Father, but by me." Jesus did not claim to show *a* way to God. He declared that only through the Cross and the grace it provides can we **FIND OUR WAY TO GOD**. In other words, if we come to know and accept Jesus, then it becomes possible to have a relationship with God.

We cannot enter into the gates of heaven until we **MAKE PEACE WITH JESUS**. Eternal life is given only to those who believe that Christ died to pay the penalty for their sin and that He rose again. If we are self-righteous and think we are good, we will not enter until we repent. If we have hated, the Bible says it is the same as committing murder in our hearts. If we blaspheme, or have taken God's name in vain, we have sinned. Yet despite all of our sins, Jesus suffered on the cross for us. All we have to do to receive our inheritance of everlasting life is to genuinely repent.

Don't sell short the opportunity to spend eternity in heaven. No matter how beautifully designed heaven is, it is no better than earth unless God is there. We can build beautiful, amazing, expensive mansions and cities. Travel the world and you will find beauty that seems without compare. No matter how beautiful it is, without God it is still not enough to completely satisfy our souls. The goal shouldn't be just about getting to heaven. The goal should be to finally *know* your Creator. When you speak with the young ones in your life about heaven, be sure to tell them the best part—the part about actually **LIVING WITH GOD HIMSELF!**

Father in heaven, I thank You for making salvation
so simple—so easy to know that I will someday be with
You in heaven. By grace, I look forward to the day when
I can live in the beauty of Your presence.

PART FIVE

Celebrate Your Life

ENJOYING A HEALTH-FILLED life is the benefit of living a Spirit-led life. If you haven't discovered what your passion in life is, it is time to take a break and explore what your unique personality is designed to take delight in doing. And don't be afraid to delegate whatever others can do instead; then you will have time to experience the pleasures that money cannot buy for you. Open your life to the rejuvenation of rest and relaxation, and enjoy the people around you. It's simply a healthy thing to do.

Your Mission for Life

I will instruct you and teach you in the way
you should go; I will guide you with My eye.

—PSALM 32:8 (NKJV)

This verse from Psalm 32 makes it clear that God is willing and more than able to guide our life path. He longs to guide us with love and wisdom. He offers His knowledge for our best life pathway. The problem is that many of us have never bothered to even ask God what kind of plans He has for our lives.

It's interesting to think about your life and the direction it has taken in relation to what may have influenced that direction. Our parents obviously play a big role in our career choices and development. My mom was an artist until the reality of finances and rearing six children took precedence over art. It was only natural for Mom to want all of us to have an appreciation for art. Mom always said that I was the least artistic of her six children. I was the brainy one. Math and science concepts just came naturally to me. Yet in spite of the ease with which those subjects came for me, my heart yearned for artistic expression. From the time I was seven, I knew I wanted to be an interior designer, but my path to design was not direct.

Guidance counselors kept Mom and Dad convinced that my aptitude for the sciences was a concrete indication of what my career should be. In college, I found myself with a major in chemical engineering. After working five years in that field, I had the courage to say no, and quit. Finally, I pursued my passion and went back to school to get my design degree. My artistic ability is my skill in expressing what I see in my mind through design and decoration, it is not in drawing or painting. My parents, teachers and the guidance counselors all had very good intentions for me. An engineering degree would afford me a very nice living. In fact, I would probably be retired right now. But as good and wise as all who guided me were, they could never be as wise as God.

Sometimes, parents and counselors are completely tuned into God's plans for our lives. If we follow their advice, we end up doing exactly what God wants for us. Other times, God's plans may include "seasonal" work. In other words, God takes us on a path for a while to teach us specific things necessary for His future plans for our lives. At this time in my life, God wants me to write. My years of working as an interior designer gave me the opportunity to establish intimate and meaningful relationships with many people. It is through the sharing of their lives, wisdom, fears and joys that I have been prepared for this new task that God has given me.

WHAT IS YOUR LIFE MISSION?

All the experts tell us that we need to have a mission statement to guide our lives. But unless our mission statement is in line with God's mission for our lives, we will have limited or no success at all. In order to fulfill God's plans, we must first know what they are. This requires spending time with God by reading His word, asking Him specific questions, and listening for His answers. The more we know Him, the more we will know ourselves.

Romans 12:2 says God will transform you into a new person by changing the way you think. Only then will you know what God wants you to do. If you seek to be close to God, He will show you the purpose He has for your life. In other words, if you seek first His kingdom and His righteousness for your life, all things will be given to you (see Matthew 6:32–34, NIV).

God has given you talent. Your individual talents are a clear message from God for your life paths. If you have the talent for leadership, then your God-chosen path will require the ability to lead. Your talent is just one of the tools that God gives you to succeed with His plans. You must also be obedient.

A friend of mine felt God was calling him to leave a secure job as a professor at a Bible college and go into the ministry. With four young sons to raise, his wife was concerned for their future security. She said she felt a bit like Noah's wife asking, "Are you sure He said 'ark' and not 'park'?" Building a park sounded like a far more reasonable idea. But none of us would be here now if Noah had built a park instead of an ark. My friend is now assistant pastor at a very large seeker church. It is clearly God's plan for him to be there. God has given him the perfect personality and ability to draw young people to the Lord.

Following God's path requires obedience, even when it doesn't make sense to us. Remember Sarah and her attempt at fulfilling God's promise of children to her? Instead of allowing God to be in charge to provide her with a child, she took things into her own hands—and what a mess she made!

Sarah found herself despised by her handmaiden and lost out on the many blessings God wanted to give her.

Fear can also keep us from accomplishing the plans that God has for us, either fear of failure or fear of inadequacy. We *think* we are not capable or smart enough to take on such work, but what we forget is we are not doing this alone. God would never ask us to do something without giving us everything we need to succeed. As Ed Gray wrote in his book, *Forty Days to a Life of Gold*, "When we don't believe in the gifts and ideas that God has placed inside us, we step outside our callings to find success. Even if you do find success outside your calling, you won't *feel* successful. And your work will not bring glory to God; it is not what the Lord made you to do."[30]

It is only when we believe in the talent God has given us and use it for His glory that we can truly find fulfillment in our lives. Jesus is our best example of someone following the path God had for Him. Just think how often Jesus turned to His Father for guidance.

John the Baptist set an example for us when he said of Jesus, "He must increase, but I must decrease" (John 3:30, NKJV). Jesus put God before everything, saying, "Father . . . not My will, but Yours, be done" (Luke 22:42, NKJV). Unless we surrender our will to God's will, our mission will fail no matter how hard we work or how well we plan.

As author Deborah DeFord wrote "We cannot see light; we can only see what it illuminates. God who is the Spirit, is invisible, but when God illuminates our view, we see the Divine in the visible."[31] When the Holy Spirit (Who is in us) gives us new sight, we see, and everything becomes clear. When we can finally see God's plan, our lives take on new meaning. Our lives become a living worship that brings praise and glory to God.

If you have never written a mission statement for your life, now is the time. Begin first with a clear view of God. Make this a prayer priority and let your desire be known to Him.

As you desire to see God more clearly, He will indeed make Himself known to you. So much of our self-image comes from all those around us. But until you have God's perspective of who you are, it is not complete.

SIMPLICITY MADE SIMPLE

Here are some ideas to help you find the mission God has for your life:

Unless we know the purpose that God designed us for, life will seem like nothing more than an endless weary journey. **WRITE DOWN YOUR VISION.** Pray and ask for God's guidance. Then honestly evaluate the talents you have been given. Think about what you are doing with your life right now. Do you find the work fulfilling? A purpose-driven life is fulfilling. Paul said, "I am focusing all my energies on this one thing" (Philippians 3:13–14, NLT). His mission was to press on toward the goal of winning the prize for which God had called him heavenward. Imagine how much more fulfilling and simpler your life would be if you knew the *one thing* on which God wanted you to focus.

God did not design us to live alone. God uses other people in our lives in very specific ways. All of us need **A MISSION PARTNER.** This should not be your spouse or your parent. My mission partner is my best friend Jan. I can always count on her to see the real me. She can easily point out my areas of strength and weakness. This makes it so much easier for me to know how God wants to use me and where I still need work. A mission partner will keep you accountable.

SHARE YOUR DREAMS with those you trust, but stay away from naysayers. They can be dream killers. Too often, our friends and family are more concerned with practical security. But doing the will of God often requires risk. The Word teaches that we live by faith and not by sight (2 Corinthians 5:7).

NURTURE YOUR DREAMS WITH PRAYER. God may give you the vision, but He still expects you to produce the fruit. Spend time in prayer and meditation as you prepare to take on the goal.

GOD PROMISES TO GIVE YOU ALL YOU NEED to accomplish the goal He has set for you. The Bible, the Holy Spirit and the circumstances in which He has placed you are three tools that God uses to help you become all He wants you to be. Use them!

> Lord, by faith I will step out and walk toward
> the prize that awaits me when I fulfill Your plan
> for my life. Please make clear the direction I am to go,
> and I will follow You wherever You lead me.

Who Are You?

But the fruit of the Spirit is love, joy, peace,

longsuffering, gentleness, goodness, faith,

Meekness, temperance: against such there is no law.

—GALATIANS 5:22–23 (KJV)

Who are you? How do you answer that question? In the sixties, we were often defined by our zodiac sign. I was born in January. My zodiac sign says that I'm a goat! I never quite identified with that definition. Titles are often used as a defining part of who we are. If you are a doctor, that usually puts you in high esteem. Pastors, presidents and professors also seem to have an advantage. Even if a person lacks personality, a title can make him or her important— if not cool. With the right title, your personality weaknesses can be defined as interesting quirks rather than something that needs work.

The jobs we've had certainly help define who we are, but ultimately, each of us came with very specific personality traits. Life affects us, but it's more about how we have responded to life than the experiences themselves. For example, children living in the same house with the same set of parents can have completely different responses to the same situations.

Understanding who you are and why you act the way you do can help you improve your study habits, your eating habits and how you get along with everyone in your life. God designed you for His purpose. Unless we understand our weaknesses and our strengths, we will struggle with the work He has set before us.

KNOW THYSELF

If you have ever worked for a large corporation, you probably had to take the DISC personality profile assessment test as part of the hiring process. The DISC was developed in the seventies and has gained in popularity ever since. The profile results give an employer insight into how you process information, respond to stress and how you relate with others. It can also be used to help improve your life, relationships, work productivity, teamwork and your ability to communicate. Each of the letters in the DISC represents a different personality type.

D stands for dominance. A dominant personality likes to get results, is decisive and direct, and accepts challenges well. These people are often impatient, strong willed and quick to take action.

I stands for influence. Influential personalities are people-oriented, optimistic and in need of recognition. They are also entertaining, expressive, outgoing, enthusiastic and energizing.

S stands for steadiness. A steady personality is stable, cooperative, predictable, deliberate, diplomatic, consistent, a good listener and sympathetic.

C stands for conscientious. A conscientious personality is analytical, concerned, accurate, orderly, correct, quality conscious, systematic and plans ahead.

You can find easy-to-take self-administered versions of DISC online using your computer or with the help of your local reference librarian. I encourage you to take it, even if you've done it before.

Tim LaHaye has written several books based on Hippocrates' four temperament characteristics: sanguine, choleric, melancholy and phlegmatic.

The *sanguine* man or woman is carefree and full of hope, and attributes great importance to whatever he or she may be dealing with at one moment, but may have forgotten all about it the next day.

The *choleric* person is hotheaded, quickly aroused, but easily calmed if his opponent gives in. He or she is annoyed without holding a grudge. His actions are quick but not persistent. He prefers to give orders but does not want to be bothered with carrying them out.

Melancholy types attribute great importance to everything that concerns them. They discover cause for anxiety everywhere and notice first of all the difficulties (not the possibilities) in a situation. The melancholy individual is the least happy because he is most likely to call forth opposition to himself.

The *phlegmatic* person lacks emotion. He or she is not easily or quickly moved but is persistent. Such individuals warm up slowly, but retain their warmth toward you. They act on principle, not instinct. They have a content temperament and are reasonable in their dealings with other people. They are very good at persuading others to agree with them.

When you can identify and understand your own personality, you can uncover your unique potential for your job, your marriage and your church. Guideposts writer Marilyn Morgan King offered this about the importance of knowing oneself:

One day my best friend Mona and I had lunch together, and I shared some of the problems that were showing up in my relationships. She asked a penetrating question: "Do you think you may be unconsciously choosing men who are similar to your former husband?" That night I sat for a long time in prayer and self-examination and I began to see that I'd been repeating some of the same patterns that had caused my marriage to fail. Clearly, I had work to do—on myself!

About the same time I was shopping for a new dining room table. Louise asked what furniture style I liked. The only answer I could come up with was, "I don't know!" It was another wake-up moment—in many ways I didn't really know who I was!

Over the following weeks and months, I started each morning with silent prayer, asking for self-knowledge and listening for guidance. After breakfast I spent time writing in my journal, asking such questions as: What are my priorities? How do I really want to spend the rest of my life? What might I give back to life during my remaining years? As the insights came and I tried to follow the guidance I received during prayer, my sense of independence grew. Gradually, I began to feel more like a whole person.

Then one day I found the perfect dining room set for my house, a cottage-style oak-and-tile table with country-blue legs and matching Windsor chairs that just felt right. For me, it was a small symbol of larger inner changes occurring in my life. At last I felt I had a clearer sense of who I was. This new awareness opened me to a deeper trust in whatever life might bring.[32]

Like Marilyn, until we know who we are, how can we expect others to know us? How can we make good decisions for our lives unless we know ourselves? It's like shopping for the perfect gift for a stranger! Ultimately, to be the best that God wants us to be is going to require living a Spirit-filled life. Without the Holy Spirit we cannot bear the fruits of *love, joy, peace, long-suffering, gentleness, goodness, faith, meekness and temperance*. Regardless of our individual personalities, we can be assured that when we submit to the Spirit, we will be capable of the best kinds of personality traits.

As Tim LaHaye says, "A singing, grateful heart and a submissive spirit, independent of circumstances, are so unnatural that they can only be ours through the filling of the Holy Spirit."[33] That fits perfectly with one of my favorite sayings, "There is no excuse for bad behavior."

SIMPLICITY MADE SIMPLE

Here are some ideas to help you better know yourself:

If you have never taken a **PERSONALITY PROFILE**, try it. Better yet, I suggest you and your mate both take it. My husband Dave and I took a premarriage course that included a personality profile. At that time I thought it was funny that his idea of the perfect vacation was spending a week in a canoe in the Canadian Wilderness and mine was a week on a sailboat in the Caribbean. When it comes time to plan a real vacation, it's no longer so funny!

Most of us are a combination of personality traits with one being more dominant and the others more recessive. Each has tremendous strengths and weaknesses. The good news is that **GOD WILL TRANSFORM** each of our weaknesses and make us better and more useful if we let Him.

THE POINT of identifying your personality traits is *not* to use them as excuses for what you do wrong. Too often, our mistakes have more to do with the choices we make rather than our personalities. The goal is to learn where you are weak and allow the Holy Spirit to work in you.

Make a list first of **YOUR STRENGTHS**. Once you have identified your strengths, make a corresponding list of your weaknesses. Be firm with yourself. All of us find it much easier to list our strengths than our weaknesses. Your career choice can give you some clues as to your personality. Sanguine types are often actors, salespeople or speakers. Cholerics are producers, builders and leaders. Melancholics usually are best suited to being artists, musicians, inventors and professors. Diplomats, accountants, teachers and techies are typically phlegmatic personalities.

The one thing about personality you can count on is that we all have one! No matter what yours is, God has a purpose for it.

> Thank you, Lord, for creating me with a unique personality suited for my purpose in life. Please help me to understand how to use my strengths and transform my weaknesses into useful service for my life mission.

The Leader Within

"Those who are wise will shine like the brightness of the
heavens, and those who lead many to righteousness,
like the stars for ever and ever."

—DANIEL 12:3 (NIV)

A s Christians we are truly blessed that no matter where we are, we have a Leader that we can always trust and depend on to lead us exactly where we should go. We can pray to God, as David did, saying, "From the end of the earth will I cry unto thee, when my heart is overwhelmed: lead me to the rock that is higher than I" (Psalm 61:2, KJV).

Life offers all of us opportunities for leadership too. It doesn't matter whether we have a job in the workforce or one at home; we still have the opportunity to lead. Whether we *choose* to lead or not is up to each of us. Many people are afraid to lead, and this can result in passive, unhealthful living. Some may lay aside the opportunity to lead others because they are afraid of the responsibility or afraid of failure. Others simply don't feel qualified to lead. That's sad, because successful leaders have simply learned how to match their personal skills to specific tasks, and that makes it easy for them to succeed. Real leaders delegate that which others can do more easily or better.

Leadership is the ability to create a vision for a new course of action or goal that is also consistent with the values of those you hope to enlist to accomplish it. I think the key word here is "values." The values of the leader are the foundation for leadership.

It is our deeply held values and principles that provide the basis for the way we lead. Helen Kendall, founder of Kendall College of Art and Design says, "True leadership is appreciated, not resented." As Christians, we have a mission to lead many people to righteousness. We also have the perfect example for the right values in Christ and the values He taught should be reflected in the way we lead.

Recently, my niece took a new job as director of activities at a resident-care facility. At twenty-three, she suddenly found herself with five employees working under her. We had a lengthy discussion about the difference between managing and leading. To manage is simply to maintain the status quo and keep things running the way they always have been run. Leadership makes changes to improve the situation.

An unattributed quote says, "The pessimist complains about the wind; the optimist expects the wind; the realist adjusts the sails." I think this is a good example of a leader. Leadership is not about charisma, forcefulness or a specific style. Leadership understands people and the process of getting people headed in the same direction. Leaders communicate a *vision* of how things could be better, and then they inspire everyone on the "team" to believe in the vision and to work together to accomplish it.

In our homes, leadership can be as simple as setting a vision of getting the house cleaned in the most efficient manner so everyone can have more leisure time. The simplest way to accomplish this task would be to match the individuals' passions and skills to the work that needs to be done. Whoever likes doing laundry should be assigned the task of getting most of the laundry done. The gardener of the household can be in charge of yard work. Good leaders inspire teamwork and cooperation. Andrew Carnegie said, "No man will ever make a great leader who wants to do it all by himself or get all the credit for doing it."

Good leaders are also flexible. Too many people view flexibility as weakness. They *think* they have to continue going in a certain direction even when it's clear that it's not working. Successful leaders realize that as situations change, they must be willing to reevaluate and change course if necessary. A good leader is a good listener and a good student—always willing to learn from others.

Guideposts writer Fred Bauer wrote an interesting piece about leadership:

A friend was lamenting the lack of leadership in the country. "We should be doing better with health care, the environment, feeding the hungry . . ." I couldn't disagree, but reminded him of an old political truism: People only get the leadership they demand. Sometimes that means taking leadership roles ourselves.

How so? By agreeing to lead the stewardship committee; by agreeing to lead the class; by agreeing to lead the PTA; by agreeing to lead a neighborhood action group. Leadership doesn't require enormous intellect, dazzling talent or superhuman strength, only commitment and a willingness to give of our God-given gifts.

There is a cemetery off the coast of Normandy in Caen, France, where many RAF [Royal Air Force] pilots are buried. They died during the early, crucial battles of World War II. One of the graves bears this great definition of leadership: "Leadership is wisdom, courage, and carelessness of self." God honors people who are careless givers of themselves.[34]

Fred Bauer makes it clear that all of us have a responsibility to lead others somewhere, or we risk being led down the wrong path. If there is something that bothers you about the way things are, it may be your assignment from God to lead in the progress to bring change.

SIMPLICITY MADE SIMPLE

Leadership starts with having a vision. A vision can be grand like that of Martin Luther King, Jr.'s manifesto or as simple as improving the life of your family.

Once you have a vision, then develop a plan to achieve it. Assess the information you have and **MATCH IT WITH THE AVAILABLE SKILLS**.

You ensure success by **CHOOSING THE RIGHT PEOPLE** for the job. Sometimes different situations require different team members.

Successful leaders **CULTIVATE INDEPENDENT THINKING**. This is especially important for families. Unless we encourage independent thinking in our children and grandchildren, we handicap them for the rest of their lives.

Instead of giving them all the answers, ask them pointed questions that will lead them to explore their own solutions. Simple questions like, "What would you do?" or "How do you think we ended up with this problem situation?" can be very helpful in getting them involved in the process and teaching them important life skills.

Although sometimes it may be easier to just do something yourself, you miss the opportunity to teach someone else. We all know it takes more time to accomplish a task while teaching someone else how to do it. But we succeed in the end, because once we teach someone else how to do it, we can delegate it! We all succeed if we delegate in ways that **ENABLE PEOPLE TO GROW**.

Sometimes we don't delegate because we like being in control. Examine yourself and look for signs that may indicate a wrong motive. Then **ASK OUR HEAVENLY LEADER FOR GUIDANCE AND FORGIVENESS**.

Leadership often involves **RISK TAKING**. Unless we take risks, we lose the opportunity for greater success in life. Weigh your options and gauge the upside. By calculating your odds of success, you may often find that the better solution involves risk taking. You may not succeed every time you take a risk, but you will eventually reap bigger rewards. As the old phrase says, "Nothing ventured, nothing gained." Just think where we would be if the Israelites never ventured into the desert!

One of the greatest challenges of leadership is **EARNING THE TRUST OF OTHERS**. People need to know who you are and what you are made of before they will follow you. The best leaders lead by example. As Christians, our lives should be a prime example of our leadership values. Ultimately, people will only follow you if they believe you have their best interests at heart.

Leadership always involves **BUILDING A SENSE OF COMMUNITY**. Your family is the foundation for our country's community. Unless you have a strong foundation in your family, we cannot have a strong foundation for our country. Great leaders constantly reinforce the vision and quickly resolve conflicts.

TAKE TIME TO KNOW YOUR TEAM. We all come from different families and different situations. If you are to lead a group in your church, work or community, you must first know and understand the team members and work with their specific characteristics. That requires listening and encouraging each team member. In the end, a good leader must have the ability to persuade, inspire, listen, surround themselves with good advisers and set priorities.

> **Lord, I desire to lead others in the way of Your righteousness. Give me boldness when I need to be bold, courage when I need to be courageous, and humility when I need to simply trust You to work in my life.**

A Day of Healthy Beauty

Do you not know that your body is the temple

of the Holy Spirit who is in you, whom you have

from God, and you are not your own? For you were

bought at a price; therefore glorify God in your body

and in your spirit, which are God's.

—1 CORINTHIANS 6:19–20 (NKJV)

Think about what would you do if you actually had the responsibility of caring for the body of the Holy Spirit? Would you rub essential oils into His skin as you massage away the stress and pain in His tight muscles? Would you suggest He take a long soak in a warm tub with water swirling round and round to the glow of lavender-scented candles? Or perhaps you would give Him a pedicure and gently remove the dirt and dry skin with a soothing sugar scrub? Guess what? You *are* in charge of the body of the Holy Spirit. Each of us is a temple of the Holy Spirit and it is necessary that we occasionally give it a little tender love and care.

If you are like me, you grew up believing luxuries such as getting a massage, manicure or pedicure were only for the rich. The reality is that massage is as old as the world itself. Jesus healed with His hands. When He laid hands on those inflicted, they were healed. His healing touch was miraculous. Today the medical community has finally recognized the healing benefits of massage too. My first introduction to massage came at the orders of an orthopedic surgeon for my elbow. I have tennis elbow from writing. Even though I use a computer to write, the repetitive movement has all but worn out my elbow. I was not a good candidate for surgery because I am not able to stop doing exactly what is causing the problem, which is working on the computer.

I was very skeptical when my physician first suggested the work of a specific massage therapist. Now, three years later, I am grateful for the strong healing hands of Emmett, my therapeutic massage therapist. It's amazing the difference it has made in my life. Each week, for one hour, Emmett inflicts pain deep into the muscles and tendons of my arm and shoulder. It's what I call good pain. It hurts at the time but it works out all the monster knots that cause my pain.

Donna is my manicurist; yes, I also allow myself the pleasure of a simple, no-polish manicure too. She recently was telling me about one of her clients. Catherine accidentally won a free manicure from Donna when she placed her silent auction slip in the wrong box. It must have been God's angels intervening because now, many years later, Catherine still comes in for a biweekly manicure. It is clear to Donna that Catherine needs the comforting touch that the physical contact of the manicure brings. You see, Catherine is elderly and lives alone. None of her family lives nearby. Donna is probably providing the only physical contact that Catherine receives. Just as children who, deprived of touch in their early years, have difficulty connecting or bonding to others, so it is for all of us.

God designed our skin with delicate sensitivity. Obviously, our sensitivity to touch serves many purposes. It keeps us from getting burned when we sense the heat of something too hot, and it provides pleasure for intimacy. But it also is a great way to eliminate stress and soothe hurting muscles with the simple act of massage.

YOU MUST TAKE CARE OF YOURSELF TO HELP OTHERS

My mom was the primary caretaker for my dad during his bout with cancer. She suffered alongside him through several years before his death. Near the end of Dad's life, Mom desperately needed a break. Since I was the only one living away from our hometown, it was decided that we would put Mom on a plane and send her to my house for a few days' respite while the rest of the family cared for Dad. Mom said it had been years since she was able to sleep more than a few hours at a time. The first thing on the agenda when Mom arrived was a massage—a full body massage. It was something Mom had never had. That night, Mom slept twelve hours! She couldn't believe it. The deep soothing massage was the perfect prescription for a much-needed rest.

My best friend Jan is a dancer. She teaches sacred dance and is a member of a dance troupe. She is amazing. At age fifty she soars higher than ever. But, like most of us, time is taking its toll. Often she suffers with pain in her feet. I was thrilled when I found a simple way to provide her with a little comfort for her feet with a pair of microwavable footies. They provide warm heat along with the healing power of lavender. It forces Jan to sit down and care for herself, even if just for a few minutes. She also enlists the strong hands of her husband to add to the anti-pain therapy. He happily massages her feet each night.

Jesus cared about our bodies enough to heal them with His touch. We also should care enough about them to allow ourselves a few simple healing luxuries. Life can be hard, and a simple massage or backrub can do wonders for body and mind.

SIMPLICITY MADE SIMPLE

ESSENTIAL OILS are a simple way to use aromatherapy to improve the quality of your life. Choose scents that make you feel good and then incorporate them into your life. Something as basic as making a candlescape and scenting it with oil is a great way to add beauty and a healing scent to your home. Since the sense of smell is one of our strongest senses, it is an easy way to calm your body and relax your mind. Patty, my assistant, made a candlescape for me. She simply took an inexpensive clear glass plate, and on it she placed three pretty pillar candles and surrounded them with shells and sea glass. Then she scented the shells and glass with beautifully fragrant oil. I have it placed on a shelf of the bookcase in my bedroom. Each time I enter, I am welcomed and calmed with this soothing gift.

A simple neck, back and shoulder massage can make the cares of the day disappear. Here are the instructions for **GIVING SUCH A MASSAGE** to someone you love: (1) Have your loved one sit on a chair sideways so you can work on his or her back. Cover the back and shoulders with a damp warm towel or use one of the microwavable pads. Then, using soft, stroking motions, move up and down the back several times to warm the muscles further. (2) Slowly rub the lower back by placing your hands wide and open on it; this allows the heat to penetrate. (3) Continue the massage by working in an upward, circular, gentle motion up the back toward the neck. Do this movement several times, allowing muscles to relax. (4) Rub the neck by placing your fingers on one side of the neck, with your thumb on the other side. Use small circular motions moving in and out, pulling the tension from the neck. Repeat several times. Then teach this method to your loved one and get him or her to give you a massage!

A SCALP MASSAGE is also a great way to release tension. Always remember that small circular gentle motion is best. Work deep enough to move the scalp; *gently* pulling the hair can also relax the scalp muscles.

If you suffer with sinus trouble, try **A FACIAL MASSAGE**. You will be amazed at the clearing benefits of this therapy.

When looking for **PROFESSIONAL THERAPISTS**, be sure they are licensed and certified by the state in which they are practicing. Most professionals will work with you at your own comfort level. You do not have to get naked to get a full body massage if you don't want to.

Treat yourself and a friend to **A SPA DAY**! If you can't afford to actually go together for a pedicure, manicure, facial or massage, then do it for each other.

Lord, thank You for restoring my health through Your healing touch. Your Word says You will guide me always and satisfy my needs in a sun-scorched land and strengthen my frame. I receive Your healing touch so I will be like a well-watered garden, like a spring whose waters never fail (Isaiah 58:11), and look for opportunities to touch others with Your healing power.

Time to Play!

He that is of a merry heart hath a continual feast.

—PROVERBS 15:15 (KJV)

Yesterday as we drove past an elementary school, my husband said, "Remember when life was that simple. Wouldn't it be great if the only thing we had to think about at the end of the day was walking home?" As I thought about his comment, I realized that much of our unhappiness, worry and frustration comes from within ourselves. It's simply a matter of attitude. Our attitudes can color our whole perspective. We may not be able to choose the things that happen to us, but we can choose how we will respond.

The Bible says that the secret to a good attitude is to fill our minds with thoughts that are pure, true and lovely. We are to dwell on the good things in life (Philippians 4:8). When Paul faced the struggle of imprisonment, he adopted a good attitude and focused his mind on only good thoughts. He wrote, "I only know that in every city the Holy Spirit warns me that prison and hardships are facing me. However, I consider my life worth nothing to me, if only I may finish the race and complete the task the Lord Jesus has given me—the task of testifying to the gospel of God's grace" (Acts 20:23–24).

In his recent book *The Irritable Male Syndrome*, psychotherapist Jed Diamond says that just like women, men go through a midlife hormonal change that leaves most of them crabby, depressed and just plain hard to live with. Dr. Diamond believes that eighty percent of men are affected. If you are married to one of these curmudgeons, you know how difficult it can be. Women at least are willing to admit that they are having a hard time hormonally. Most guys won't even discuss it. Diamond says men need to stop defining themselves in terms of their job titles and start searching for a purpose that comes from within. (Hmmm . . . doesn't that sound a bit familiar? All of us need a good dose of this advice.) Diamond continued, "The question I'd put to an older man is, 'Now that you've done what you were supposed to do, what were you put on earth to do?'"[35] I agree and think that this is the question we all need to ask ourselves. We place too much focus on producing income, which leads us to believe that money will bring happiness.

Personal finance expert Jean Chatzky conducted a survey with the Roper Organization of America on money and happiness. She found that happiness increases with income, but only to a point. The percentage of people who say they are happy only rises as income does until it reaches about fifty thousand dollars per year. After that, they are no happier. The fact of the matter is that once we have enough money to meet our basic needs, having more money doesn't have a positive effect.

The factors that most affect our happiness are the quality of our marriages and other key relationships, self-esteem, job satisfaction and, of course, health. The survey discovered another interesting statistic: Twice as many people reported worrying about money than about their marriages, friendships, self-esteem or jobs. My response is, "Boy are we dumb if we waste all our time and effort worrying about the one thing that won't make us happy!"

Guideposts writer Brock Kidd tells an interesting story:

> In my top desk drawer is an old buckeye that my grandfather gave me many years ago. "For good luck, buddy," I remember him saying. The buckeye is a brown nut similar to a chestnut. Its surface is smooth and hard. That old buckeye acts as a perfect stress-reliever. I roll it around in my hand and suddenly I think about my grandfather.
>
> Pa was a big man, six-foot-four and barrel-chested, but he had the heart of a playful child. He would spend hours raking leaves, then pile them into a great mound and take a running leap into the pile, his big body scattering leaves everywhere. And more than once I'd seen him turn from some summer project to escape the heat with a quick dive in the lake—with all of his clothes on!
>
> Food was another of Pa's great joys. He loved to cook, and he'd make wonderful things with cheeses and meats and vegetables, always delicious. Whenever he took me out to eat, he insisted on my ordering the most adventurous thing on the menu. While other five-year-olds were eating hamburgers from the children's menu, I was tackling a whole lobster or figuring out just exactly how to eat an artichoke leaf.
>
> So here I am in my office, rubbing my buckeye and remembering. By now, almost everyone else has gone home. I

look out the window and see a worker blowing leaves off the city sidewalk and I know just what I'm going to do. In thirty minutes I'm home, out of my suit and into my jeans. "Harrison," I say to my ten-month-old (he's named after Pa), "how about coming outside with Daddy and raking some leaves?"[36]

It sounds to me that Brock's Pa had a very good attitude, which kept him from becoming a grumpy old man!

Benjamin Franklin was also said to have known the secret to happiness. Did you know he was nearly sixty years old when he began his political career? It's true. It's clear that Franklin was a strong visionary. He developed a plan for a new country. His plan for an independent America made life happier for all of us. Franklin had passion. His passion for ideas is what gave him the ability to make some of the greatest discoveries. If it weren't for his kite experiment, we might all still be living in the dark.

Ben Franklin was known to cultivate friendships. While living in Philadelphia, he organized the Junto, which was a club for discussing intellectual topics such as the difference between knowledge and prudence. It was clear that Franklin knew his strengths and used them to his best ability. They say he listened more than he spoke. In fact, he is not known for one single important public speech! Instead, he encouraged others to bring out their own ideas. It's well known that Franklin had many enemies. But rather than fight with them, he chose to ignore them and move on.

Franklin also could have been one of the richest men of his time. Instead, once he had enough to meet his basic needs, he stopped pursuing wealth and focused on the things that gave him greater enjoyment such as friends, new ideas and investment in our great nation. He is also credited with this quote, "Keep your eyes wide open before marriage, half shut afterward." I think Benny was a very wise man!

As the Bible says, there is a time for everything. And sometimes you just have to take time for a little R & R. We could all learn to be a bit more spontaneous and say yes to spur-of-the-moment invitations from our kids and grandkids. Better yet—rather than waiting for an engraved invitation—go ask them to come out and play. I'm sure they'll be thrilled you asked.

SIMPLICITY MADE SIMPLE

Here are some other inspirations for living a happy, healthy life:

LOOK AT YOUR ATTITUDE and examine what you allow to enter your mind and what you choose to think about. You may be in need of a thought overhaul. Noted comedian Jonathan Winters said, "I couldn't wait for success . . . so I went ahead without it!" Now that's what I call the right attitude for the job.

The next time you pass someone sitting alone on a bench, stop and take a seat beside him or her. Who knows—this could be the chance for **MAKING A NEW LIFETIME FRIEND**.

Look for opportunities to **BE AN EARTH ANGEL**; it's very rewarding! I travel a lot by plane, and I always look for an opportunity to meet someone new or help someone who looks a bit down. I call this my "wing-and-a-prayer ministry." God amazes me with the opportunities He has made for this little ministry. During one trip I saw a woman sleeping on a set of chairs at the airport. She looked like a homeless person, but I felt a nudge from the Spirit encouraging me to approach her. When I did, I discovered that she was a cross-country truck driver whose mother had died the night before. The problem was that the truck-driving lady was in Pennsylvania and her mother lived in California. Together, we found a way to get her on my plane to California; unfortunately, there was only room on the plane to get her to Chicago. God then provided a seat on another plane headed to John Wayne airport in Southern California. In addition, God also provided a wonderful older couple to escort her along the way.

GET YOUR FINANCES IN ORDER. The Roper Organization survey found that those who set specific goals and made choices to implement those financial goals were happier. Most of us don't know how much money we are spending or how much we will need for our later years. But we won't be able to manage or plan for our future until we know the facts. Did you know that when couples fight with each other about money, it's really a fight about goals? Unless they are both working toward the same goal regarding money, they will never stop fighting about it.

SET CLEAR INTENTIONS. Sit quietly and write down your personal desires for the different aspects of your life. Consider your relationship needs, career and financial needs, and your spiritual goals. Then pray for guidance on how God wants you to proceed.

BE GRATEFUL. Yes, happiness is really about whether you see the glass as half full or half empty. Every day spend some time thinking about all the good things and people in your life for which you can be grateful. Keep those grumpy complaints from entering your mind. Ultimately, your happiness is your choice. Make a decision today to be happy!

Lord, thank You for making clear to me that there is time to play and time to rest, even when I know there is more work to do. You have promised wisdom, knowledge and happiness to us (Ecclesiastes 2:26), and I commit that from this day forth, I will take better care of my health while teaching others to rest in Your care too.

Conclusion

I recently enjoyed the refreshment of simple living on a morning walk in West Virginia. My husband and I were spending the weekend with his parents who were celebrating their fiftieth wedding anniversary. As a beach lover, I found that this mountainous getaway was an unusual place for me. During my walk, I discovered breathtaking beauty each step of the way. When I started, the air was crisp and my step slow. Wild cotton was growing alongside the road, and I stopped to take a closer look at it. I picked a cotton boll and was amazed by its delicate quality. I am inspired to think that this soft, silky, white fiber becomes the fabric that serves our lives with so many uses.

As I headed up the mountain, I was delighted by the view of the gentle morning light that rippled on the still water of the lake below. Birds and crickets sounded a symphony, and I felt my speed pick up as my body became more flexible with each step. I noticed that my breathing became stronger too—a good sign that my heart was getting a cardiovascular workout.

The leaves were halfway through their transition to fall colors. A giant old oak tree's leaves were just beginning to turn from green to gold. I watched as a hawk soared toward the mountaintop. The path eventually took me downhill again to the lakeshore, where cherry trees were still forcing blooms, even in October. I stopped again to study one of the blooms and I noticed that its petals looked like glass; they were almost transparent. As I counted twelve delicate petals, I was reminded of life's seasons as they cycle through a perfect year.

It was good to take time for this walk. I will revisit the healthy memory of that day when I need respite from the busy routine that life will surely bring to me again. Living in good health is like taking a walk; sometimes the path is smooth and downhill with a light breeze to cool you, and other times maintaining good health is an uphill climb with gale-force winds at your face. On the road to healthy living, there is something worthwhile every step of the way. The uphill climbs will strengthen you and give you appreciation for the simpler times.

As you walk through your life journey, remember to take time to keep your mind, body and spirit healthy. Be flexible. A flexible mind will gain wisdom from others, a flexible body will carry you all your days, and a flexible spirit will be available for the work God has ordained for you—you don't want to miss it!

Notes

Part One—You Are Wonderfully Made

1. David M. Garner, "Body Image Survey Results," *Psychology Today* (February 1997).

2. M. Tiggemann and A. S. Pickering, "Role of television in adolescent women's body dissatisfaction and drive for thinness," *International Journal of Eating Disorders* (1996): 20, 199–203, *USA Today* (August 12, 1996), 1D.

3. J. J. Brumberg, *The Body Project: An Intimate History of American Girls* (New York: Random House, 1997).

4. Tiggemann and Pickering, "Role of television."

5. M. Scott Peck, *The Road Less Traveled* (New York: Simon & Schuster, 1978), 286.

6. (Grand Rapids, Michigan: Inspirio, 2004), 169.

7. Lawrence O. Richards, PhD, *Revell Bible Dictionary* (Grand Rapids, Michigan: Fleming H. Revell, Co., 1990), 392–393.

8. Arthur Agatston, MD, *The South Beach Diet* (Emmaus, Pennsylvania: Rodale, 2003), 57.

Part Two—There Is a Rhythm to Life

9. Teresa Schantz, in *Daily Guideposts, 1991* (Carmel, New York: Guideposts, 1990), 306.

10. Ad Crable, *Lancaster New Era* (July 19, 2004), B1.

11. Dawn Groves, *Bottom Line Personal* (October 15, 2003).

12. Adapted from *Revell Bible Dictionary*, 1036.

13. Dr. Jay Lombard, Dr. Christian Renna, and Armin A. Brott, *Balance Your Brain, Balance Your Life* (New York: John Wiley & Sons, Inc., November 2003).

14. Og Mandino, *University of Success* (New York: Bantam Books, August 1983), 65.

15. Ibid., 110.

Part Three—The Greatest of All Is Love

16. Hal Urban, *Life's Greatest Lessons* (New York: Fireside, 2003), 55–63.

17. See the June 2004 archive for Darwinmag.com.

18. Bruce Bickle and Stan Jantz, *Simple Matters* (Urichville, Ohio: Promise Press, 2001), 95.

19. Kim Thomas, *Simplicity* (Nashville, Tennessee: Broadman & Holman Publishers, 1999), 82.

20. Oscar Greene in *Daily Guideposts, 1990* (Carmel, New York: Guideposts, 1989), 298.

Part Four—God Has a Health Plan for You

21. Brent Curtis and John Eldredge, *The Sacred Romance* (Nashville, Tennessee: Thomas Nelson, 1997), 5.

22. Robert Benson, *Living Prayer* (New York: Penguin Putnam, 1998), 65.

23. Lynn Morrissey, *Love Letters to God* (Sisters, Oregon: Multnomah Publishers, 2004), 5–6.

24. Eleanor Sass in *Daily Guideposts, 1989* (Carmel, New York: Guideposts, 1988), 102.

25. W. Phillip Keller, *Serenity* (Grand Rapids, Michigan: Baker Book House, 1992), 46.

26. Phyllis Hobe in *Daily Guideposts, 1993* (Carmel, New York: Guideposts, 1992), 29–30.

27. Barbara Chafin in *Daily Guideposts, 1992* (Carmel, New York: Guideposts, 1991), 281.

28. Carol Kuykendall in *Daily Guideposts, 1992* (Carmel, New York: Guideposts, 1991), 130.

29. Larry Crabb, *Shattered Dreams* (Colorado Springs, Colorado: Waterbrook Press, 2001), 181.

Part Five—Celebrate Your Life

30. Ed Gray, *Forty Days to a Life of Gold* (Valley Forge, Pennsylvania: Judson Press, 2004), 26.

31. Deborah DeFord, *"Seeking a Simpler Spirit,"* *Readers Digest* (General Books, USA, 1999), 219.

32. Marilyn Morgan King in *Daily Guideposts, 2001* (Carmel, New York: Guideposts, 2000), 82.

33. Tim LaHaye, *Why You Act the Way You Do* (Wheaton, Illinois: Tyndale House Publishers, 1984), 108.

34. Fred Bauer in *Daily Guideposts, 1999* (Carmel, New York: Guideposts, 1998), 49–50.

35. Jed Diamond, *The Irritable Male Syndrome* (Emmaus, Pennsylvania: Rodale Press, 2004).

36. Brock Kidd in *Daily Guideposts, 2002* (Carmel, New York: Guideposts, 2001), 322–323.